Revision

C000157470

GCSE Mathematics

Intermediate Tier

Stafford Burndred

Consultant Editor: Brian Seager, Chairman of Examiners

GCSE Mathematics

Name...

Address ....

....

Date of exams: (1) ....

                                      (2) ....

                                      Aural ....

Coursework deadline dates: (1) ....

                                      (2) ....

Exam board ....

Syllabus number...

Candidate number ....

Centre number ....

Further copies of this publication, as well as the guides for Foundation and Higher tiers may be obtained from:

Pearson Publishing
Chesterton Mill, French's Road, Cambridge CB4 3NP
Tel 01223 350555   Fax 01223 356484

Email info@pearson.co.uk   Web site http://www.pearson.co.uk/education/

ISBN: 1 85749 376 1

Published by Pearson Publishing 1996
© Pearson Publishing 1997

Revised 1997
Reprinted 1998

Contents

Introduction vi

Examiner's tips vii

Number skills
☐ Negative numbers.. 1

Maths without a calculator
☐ Mental arithmetic shortcuts – 1 2
☐ Mental arithmetic shortcuts – 2 3
☐ Decimals.. 4
☐ Long multiplication and division 5
☐ Checking – 1 6
☐ Checking – 2 7

Calculator skills
☐ Using a calculator: Brackets and memory........................... 8
☐ Using a calculator: Powers, roots, memory....................... 9
☐ Standard form 10

Fractions, decimals, percentages and ratio
☐ Fractions... 11
☐ Changing between decimals and percentages 12
☐ Changing between decimals, percentages and fractions.. 13
☐ Ratio – 1 14
☐ Ratio – 2 15
☐ Percentages.. 16
☐ Percentages and fractions..................................... 17

Number patterns
☐ Exploring number patterns (the nth term) 18
☐ Patterns you must recognise............................... 19
☐ Product of primes, highest common factor, lowest common multiple and reciprocals 20

Formulae
☐ Writing in algebra 21
☐ Using algebra 22

Equations
☐ Rules... 23
☐ Writing equations... 24
☐ Trial and improvement 25
☐ Harder equations 26
☐ Rewriting formulae 27

Algebraic skills
☐ Using algebraic formulae 28
☐ Expansion of brackets 29
☐ Factorisation – 1 30
☐ Factorisation – 2... 31
☐ Simultaneous equations: Solving using algebra 33

Contents

Graphs
- ☐ Drawing lines 34
- ☐ Simultaneous equations: Solving by drawing a graph 35
- ☐ The straight line equation y = mx + c 36
- ☐ Drawing graphs 37
- ☐ Speed, time and distance graphs 38
- ☐ Inequalities 39

Angles
- ☐ Using a protractor 40
- ☐ Angles: Acute, obtuse, reflex 41
- ☐ Intersecting and parallel lines 42
- ☐ Regular polygons 43
- ☐ Bearings 44

2-D and 3-D shapes
- ☐ 2-D representations of 3-D shapes 45
- ☐ Properties of quadrilaterals 46
- ☐ Properties of quadrilaterals and triangles 47

Similarity
- ☐ Similarity 48

Symmetry
- ☐ Rotational symmetry 49
- ☐ Symmetry of 2-D shapes 50

Transformations
- ☐ Enlargement 52
- ☐ Enlargement by a fractional scale factor 54
- ☐ Translations 55

Measurement
- ☐ Rough metric equivalents of Imperial units 56
- ☐ Converting one metric unit to another 57
- ☐ Making sensible estimates 58
- ☐ Accuracy of measurement 59
- ☐ Compound measures 60
- ☐ Time 61

Circles
- ☐ Formulae 62

Perimeter, area and volume
- ☐ Calculating length, area and volume – 1 63
- ☐ Calculating length, area and volume – 2 64
- ☐ Calculating length, area and volume – 3 65
- ☐ Formulae for length, area and volume 66

Pythagoras' theorem and trigonometry
- ☐ Pythagoras' theorem 67
- ☐ Trigonometry: Finding an angle 68
- ☐ Trigonometry: Finding a side 69
- ☐ Trigonometry: Solving problems 70

Locus
- ☐ Locus (plural loci) 71

Questionnaires   ☐ Designing questionnaires... 72
                          ☐ Hypotheses 73

Tables and graphs   ☐ Using and drawing conclusions from graphs.................... 74
                          ☐ Frequency tables and frequency diagrams....................... 75
                          ☐ Comparing data.. 76

Averages   ☐ Median and mode.. 77
                          ☐ Mean and range... 78
                          ☐ Comparing two sets of data 79
                          ☐ Grouped data.. 80

Cumulative frequency ☐ Cumulative frequency 81
                          ☐ Using cumulative frequency diagrams
                             to compare distributions.................................... 82

Scatter diagrams   ☐ Scatter diagrams 83
                          ☐ Line of best fit 84

Pie charts   ☐ Understanding pie charts.................................... 85
                          ☐ Drawing pie charts 86

Probability   ☐ The probability scale... 87
                          ☐ Justifying probabilities 88
                          ☐ Estimation of probability by experiment 89
                          ☐ Probability: Examination-type questions........................... 90
                          ☐ Probability (and, or).. 91
                          ☐ Probability (at least)....................................... 92
                          ☐ Tree diagrams... 93

Sample exam questions ☐ 94
                          Answers... 96

Diagnostic tests   Diagnostic tests 97
                          Answers.. 111

Coursework   The following pages may be useful:
                          Number patterns 18-19
                          Questionnaires... 72-73
                          Analysing and presenting data............................... 74-86

Aural test   The following pages may be useful:
                          Mental arithmetic.. 2-7

Introduction

The aim of this guide is to ensure you pass your exam and maybe even achieve a higher grade than you expect to. Ask your teacher to explain any points that you don't understand. You will have to work hard at your revision. Just reading this book will not be enough. You should also try to work through the tests at the back and any past papers that your teacher might set you to ensure that you get enough practice.

Remember it is your guide, so you may decide to personalise it, make notes in the margin, use the checklist in the contents to assess your progress, etc.

You may also find it useful to mark or highlight important sections, pages or questions you find difficult. You can then look at these sections again later.

The guide is divided into 94 short topics to make it easy to revise. Try to set aside time every week to do some revision at home.

The guide is pocket-sized to make it easy to carry. Use it wherever you have time to spare, eg registration, break, etc.

Using the guide

It may help you to place a blank piece of paper over the answers. Then read the notes and try the questions.

Do your working out and answers on the blank piece of paper. Don't just read the answers. Compare your answers with the worked answer. If your answer is wrong read the page again and then mark or make a note of the question or page. You will need to try the question again at a later date.

If you need to look up a topic to revise, try using the contents pages, or even better, the index at the back of the book.

The diagnostic tests

Diagnostic tests and answers are provided at the back of the book. You should use these to identify your weaknesses.

The author has been teaching at this level for over 20 years and is an experienced examiner.

Examiner's tips

Success in exams depends in no small part on how you approach the actual papers on the day. The following suggestions are designed to improve your exam technique.

- Read carefully the instructions on the paper.

- If you only have to answer some of the questions, read the questions and choose which to do.

- If the instructions say "Answer all the questions", work steadily through the paper, leaving out any questions you cannot do. Return to these later.

- Read each question carefully to be sure what it is you are required to do.

- If your examination includes an oral test, be sure to follow the instructions and listen carefully. For some parts you must write down only the answer – no working!

- Set out all your work carefully and neatly and make your method clear. If the examiner can see what you have done, they will be able to give marks for the correct method even if you have the answer wrong.

- If you have to write an explanation as your answer, try to keep it short.

- There will be a list of formulae at the front of the question paper. Make sure you know what is on it, and what is not – you will have to remember those!

- Check your answers, especially numerical ones. Look to see if your answers are sensible.

- Make sure you know how to use your calculator. They don't all work in the same way. Use the instruction book for your calculator when you are learning but don't take it into the exam.

- When doing a calculation, keep all the figures shown on your calculator until the end. Only round off the final answer.

- Sometimes, in a later part of a question, you need to calculate using an earlier answer. Use all the figures in the calculator display. If you use a rounded answer it could cause an error.

- Make sure you take all the equipment you may need to the exam: pens, pencils, rubber, ruler, compasses, angle measurer and calculator – make sure that the battery is working.

- When you have completed the exam, check to see that you have not missed out any questions, especially on the back page.

Examiner's tips

Exam questions often use these words:

"Show your working"
You must show your working. If you give a correct answer without working you will receive no marks.

"Do not use a calculator"
You must show enough working to convince the examiner that you have not used a calculator. (But you should still check your answer with a calculator.)

"Check using an approximation" or *"estimate"* or *"give an approximate answer"*
You must show your method and working.

"Compare"
If you are asked to compare two sets of data you must refer to both sets of data and not just one set.

Avoiding panic

If you have done your revision you have no need to panic. If you find the examination difficult, so will everyone else. This means that the pass mark will be lower.

If you cannot do a question, move on and don't worry about it. Often the answer will come to you a few minutes later.

If panic occurs, try to find a question you can do. Success will help to calm your nerves.

The consultant editor is at the very hub of setting and marking GCSE Mathematics, being Chairman of Examiners after many years as a Chief Examiner.

Number skills

We use numbers every day of our lives. You need to be confident in the basic number skills.

Negative numbers

For easy examples think of a thermometer. For difficult numbers learn how to use the $[^+/_-]$ key on your calculator. For example:

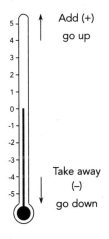

4 is a larger number than 3

3 is a larger number than 2

But look what happens when numbers are negative.

–3 is a larger number than –4

–4 is a larger number than –5

Try these:

–4 + 3   Start at –4   Add 3 means go up 3   = –1

2 – 5   Start at 2   Take away 5 means go down 5   = –3

Questions

1   Place these numbers in order, largest first:

   –3   6   –7   0   4

2   –6 + 8 =   3   –1 – 4 =

Answers

1   6, 4, 0, –3, –7   2   Start at –6 go up 8 = 2

3   Start at –1 go down 4 = –5

Using a calculator for negative numbers

First find the $[^+/_-]$ key.

Question	Calculator sequence	Answer
–3 + 7 =	$[3]\,[^+/_-]\,[+]\,[7]\,[=]$	4
–5 – –6 =	$[5]\,[^+/_-]\,[-]\,[6]\,[^+/_-]\,[=]$	1
–4 + –3 =	$[4]\,[^+/_-]\,[+]\,[3]\,[^+/_-]\,[=]$	–7
–3 x –4 =	$[3]\,[^+/_-]\,[x]\,[4]\,[^+/_-]\,[=]$	12
4 x –7 =	$[4]\,[x]\,[7]\,[^+/_-]\,[=]$	–28
$\dfrac{-6}{-2}$ =	$[6]\,[^+/_-]\,[\div]\,[2]\,[^+/_-]\,[=]$	3

1

Maths without a calculator

We had a power cut in my local supermarket. Unbelievably it had to close because no-one knew how to add up and work out change without a cash register! In the following section you will be shown all of the old methods and some shortcuts too.

If a question states "do not use a calculator," or "estimate" you **must** show your working because a correct answer without working will earn **no** marks.

Remember: Always check your answer with a calculator

Questions in this section "Maths without a calculator" should be revised before your aural test, ie mental arithmetic test. In an aural test, where you are not allowed a calculator, working is not required.

Ask your teacher if your GCSE exam includes an aural test

Mental arithmetic shortcuts – 1

Large numbers with several noughts on the end are very clumsy to work with. It is easier to take away the noughts and work with smaller numbers.

Multiplying and dividing whole numbers by 10, 100, 1000

You know 3 x 4 = 12

To work out 30 x 400 multiply 3 x 4 then add the noughts

$$30 \times 400 = 12000$$

1 nought + 2 noughts = 3 noughts

You know 21 ÷ 7 = 3

To work out 21000 ÷ 70 divide 21 ÷ 7 then take away the noughts

$$21000 \div 70 = 300$$

3 noughts − 1 nought = 2 noughts

Questions

1 4800 ÷ 60 =

2 7000 x 40 =

Answers

1 4800 ÷ 60 = 80   Answer 80
   2 noughts − 1 nought = 1 nought
2 7000 x 40 = 280 000   Answer 280 000
   3 noughts + 1 nought = 4 noughts

Mental arithmetic shortcuts – 2

These shortcuts are very useful in everyday life. Using metric units (eg for length, mass, capacity) is easier if you can multiply and divide by 10, 100 and 1000.

The number of noughts tells you how many places to move the decimal point.
1 nought = 1 place, 2 noughts = 2 places, 3 noughts = 3 places, etc.

Multiplying and dividing decimals by 10, 100, 1000

Multiplying and dividing by 10, 100, 1000 can be worked out without using a calculator.

Multiplying

By 10   Move the decimal point one place to the right

$$3 \cdot 874 \times 10 = 38\overset{\frown}{7}4 = 38 \cdot 74$$

By 100   Move the decimal point two places to the right

$$64 \cdot 3 \times 100 = 643\overset{\frown\frown}{0} = 6430$$

By 1000   Move the decimal point three places to the right

$$7 \cdot 2694 \times 1000 = 726\overset{\frown\frown\frown}{9}4 = 7269 \cdot 4$$

Dividing

By 10   Move the decimal point one place to the left

$$58 \cdot 2 \div 10 = 5\overset{\frown}{8}2 = 5 \cdot 82$$

By 100   Move the decimal point two places to the left

$$43 \cdot 62 \div 100 = 0\overset{\frown\frown}{4}362 = 0 \cdot 4362$$

By 1000   Move the decimal point three places to the left

$$2 \cdot 85 \div 1000 = 0\overset{\frown\frown\frown}{0}0285 = 0 \cdot 00285$$

Questions

1 3.61 x 100 =   2   0.42 x 1000 =

3 5.7 ÷ 100 =   4   27 ÷ 1000 =

Answers

1   $36\overset{\frown\frown}{1} = 361$

2   $0\overset{\frown\frown\frown}{4}20 = 420$

3   $0\overset{\frown\frown}{0}57 = 0 \cdot 057$

4   $0\overset{\frown\frown\frown}{0}27 = 0 \cdot 027$

Decimals

If you do not have a calculator you may need to use pen and paper methods. The same applies for aurals (mental arithmetic tests) and certain written exam questions.

Addition and subtraction of decimals

When adding or subtracting decimals remember to keep the decimal points in a straight line.

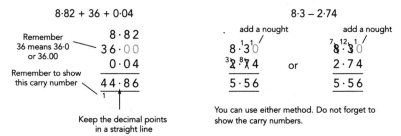

$8.82 + 36 + 0.04$

Remember
36 means 36·0
or 36.00

Remember to show
this carry number

$$\begin{array}{r} 8\cdot82 \\ 36\cdot00 \\ 0\cdot04 \\ \hline 44\cdot86 \\ {}_1 \end{array}$$

Keep the decimal points
in a straight line

$8.3 - 2.74$

add a nought   add a nought

or

You can use either method. Do not forget to show the carry numbers.

Multiplication of decimals without a calculator

3.82   Remove the decimal points. The sum is then: 382
x 0.4   x 4
                                                            ─────
                                                            1528

Count how many digits are after the decimal points in the question. There are 3 digits after the decimal points (8, 2 and 4). Therefore there will be 3 digits after the decimal point in the answer. The answer is 1.528

Division of decimals without a calculator

$3.8 \div 0.04$

We must get rid of the decimal point in the number after the ÷ sign. We move the decimal point 2 places to the right to make $0\cdot\overgroup{04}$ into 4.

We have moved the decimal point 2 places after the ÷ sign. We must do exactly the same before the ÷ sign.

We move the decimal point 2 places to the right to make $3\cdot\overgroup{80}$ into 380.

The sum is now 380 ÷ 4. The answer is 95.

Question

$0\cdot8\,|\,\overline{0\cdot52}$

Answer

$0\cdot\overset{\frown}{8}\,|\,\overline{0\cdot\overset{\frown}{5}2}$ ⟶ $8\,|\,\overline{5\cdot20}$

Put the decimal point in the answer directly above the decimal point in the question. If required you can add noughts. The answer is 0.65.

$$\begin{array}{r} 0\cdot65 \\ 8\,\overline{|\,5\cdot2^{4}0} \end{array}$$

Long multiplication and division

Sometimes you are asked to work out an answer without a calculator. Show your working and you will get your marks. (Then check with a calculator.)

Non-calculator methods for long multiplication and division

You must show all of your working to prove that you have not used a calculator.

Long multiplication

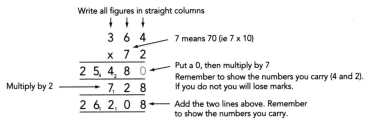

Write all figures in straight columns

$$\begin{array}{r} 3 \quad 6 \quad 4 \\ \times \quad 7 \quad 2 \\ \hline 2 \ 5_4 \ 4_2 \ 8 \ 0 \\ 7_1 \ 2 \ 8 \\ \hline 2 \ 6_1 \ 2_1 \ 0 \ 8 \end{array}$$

7 means 70 (ie 7 x 10)

Put a 0, then multiply by 7
Remember to show the numbers you carry (4 and 2).
If you do not you will lose marks.

Multiply by 2

Add the two lines above. Remember to show the numbers you carry.

The answer is 26208.

Long division

Calculate 789 ÷ 27. First write down the 27 times table.

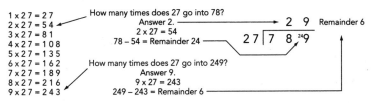

1 x 27 = 27
2 x 27 = 54
3 x 27 = 81
4 x 27 = 108
5 x 27 = 135
6 x 27 = 162
7 x 27 = 189
8 x 27 = 216
9 x 27 = 243

How many times does 27 go into 78?
Answer 2.
2 x 27 = 54
78 – 54 = Remainder 24

How many times does 27 go into 249?
Answer 9.
9 x 27 = 243
249 – 243 = Remainder 6

2 9 Remainder 6

$27 \overline{\smash{)}7\ 8\ ^{24}9}$

On some calculators you can produce the 27 times table using these keys: [2] [7] [+] [+]
Then keep pressing [=] This will produce 27, 54, 81, 108...

Questions

1 547 x 38 =

2 874 ÷ 32 =

Answers

1
$$\begin{array}{r} 5 \quad 4 \quad 7 \\ \times \quad 3 \quad 8 \\ \hline 1 \ 6_1 \ 4_2 \ 1 \ 0 \\ 4 \ 3_3 \ 7_5 \ 6 \\ \hline 2_1 \ 0 \ 7 \ 8 \ 6 \end{array}$$

2
2 7 Remainder 1 0

$32 \overline{\smash{)}8\ 7\ ^{23}4}$

32 times table

1 x 32 = 32
2 x 32 = 64
3 x 32 = 96
4 x 32 = 128
5 x 32 = 160
6 x 32 = 192
7 x 32 = 224
8 x 32 = 256
9 x 32 = 288

Checking – 1

The examiner will often ask you to estimate an answer. If the question says "estimate" you must show your working. Remember that "estimate" means do not use a calculator.

Checking using inverse operations and estimating using approximation

Checking using inverse operations

> Addition is the inverse (or opposite) of subtraction
>
> Subtraction is the inverse (or opposite) of addition
>
> Multiplication is the inverse (or opposite) of division
>
> Division is the inverse (or opposite) of multiplication

Estimating using approximation

You can produce an approximate answer to a question by taking round estimates of the figures involved. This makes the question easy to work out without using a calculator. For approximating round numbers to one significant figure see page 7.

Mrs Mackin bought 692 books for the Maths department at £8.95 each. She said the cost was £619.34. Without using a calculator, show how to check the answer.

Method	692 books is about 700	This method is correct also –
	£8.95 is about £9	you may have rounded £8·95 to £10
	9 x 700 = £6300	10 x 700 = £7000
	Mrs Mackin is wrong	Mrs Mackin is wrong

Whenever you check an answer, you must show your working.

Questions

1 Use inverse operations to check these answers:

a   3 8 6
    + 6 6 1
    ———
    1 0 4 7

b   5 8 2
     x 2 7
     ———
    1 5 1 3 2

2 Estimate the cost of 395 tickets to see a pop concert. Each ticket costs £19.

Answers

1 a   The inverse of addition is subtraction.   1047 − 661 = 386   The answer is correct.

   b   The inverse of multiplication is division.   15132 ÷ 27 = 560.444   The answer is wrong.

2   395 is about 400

    £19 is about £20

    400 x 20 = £8000

    The cost is about £8000.

Checking – 2

Again, show your working.

Estimating, multiplying and dividing by numbers between 0 and 1

Rounding to one significant figure (1 sig. fig.)

3725	⟶	4000
28·63	⟶	30
421·3	⟶	400

Round to one figure, then add noughts to the decimal point. Do **not** add noughts after the decimal point.

Note: 421.3 does **not** become 400.0

0·038	⟶	0·04
0·724	⟶	0·7
0·0306	⟶	0·03

Significant numbers are counted from the first non–zero figure.

Multiplying by numbers larger than 1
The answer is larger. Example: 3 x 5 = 15

Multiplying by numbers smaller than 1
The answer is smaller. Example: 3 x 0.05 = 0.15

Dividing by numbers larger than 1
The answer is smaller. Example: 800 ÷ 20 = 40

Dividing by numbers smaller than 1
The answer is larger. Example: 800 ÷ 0.2 = 4000

Questions

Estimate:

1   3127 x 493

2   3814 x 0.019

3   3957 ÷ 813

4   453 ÷ 17·3

Answers
1   3000 x 500 = 1 500 000   2   4000 x 0.02 = 80   3   4000 ÷ 800 = 5

4   Often there are several ways of estimating. Two possible answers for this question are:
   500 ÷ 20 = 25   or   450 ÷ 15 = 30

Calculator skills

Your calculator can be your best friend or your worst enemy. Spend some time learning to use it. You must buy a calculator with a fraction key $\boxed{a^b/_c}$. (You'll be shown how to use that in the *Fractions, decimals, percentages and ratio* section on page 11.) You will be shown how to use a calculator but if the keys shown do not work ask your teacher for help.

Using a calculator: Brackets and memory

Most calculators automatically use algebraic logic and can work out the answers. Your task is to use the correct keys. You need to know how to use brackets – 'Method A'. Most candidates find this method easier than 'Method B'. Method B is optional. If you find it confusing always use Method A.

Use of brackets

3 (6 + 8)   this means   3 x (6 + 8)

Calculator keys: $\boxed{3}$ $\boxed{x}$ $\boxed{(}$ $\boxed{6}$ $\boxed{+}$ $\boxed{8}$ $\boxed{)}$ $\boxed{=}$ Answer 42

(8 – 5) 3   this means   (8 – 5) x 3

Calculator keys: $\boxed{(}$ $\boxed{8}$ $\boxed{-}$ $\boxed{5}$ $\boxed{)}$ $\boxed{x}$ $\boxed{3}$ $\boxed{=}$ Answer 9

Questions involving division

Method A: Using brackets

$\dfrac{3{\cdot}86 - 4{\cdot}23}{7{\cdot}25 \times 3{\cdot}68}$ Place brackets at the start and end of the top line $\dfrac{(3{\cdot}86 - 4{\cdot}23)}{(7{\cdot}25 \times 3{\cdot}68)}$
  Place brackets at the start and end of the bottom line

Calculator keys: $\boxed{(}$ $\boxed{3}$ $\boxed{\cdot}$ $\boxed{8}$ $\boxed{6}$ $\boxed{-}$ $\boxed{4}$ $\boxed{\cdot}$ $\boxed{2}$ $\boxed{3}$ $\boxed{)}$ $\boxed{\div}$

$\boxed{(}$ $\boxed{7}$ $\boxed{\cdot}$ $\boxed{2}$ $\boxed{5}$ $\boxed{x}$ $\boxed{3}$ $\boxed{\cdot}$ $\boxed{6}$ $\boxed{8}$ $\boxed{)}$ $\boxed{=}$

Answer – 0·013868065

Method B: Using the memory

First work out the answer to the bottom line (remember to press =).
Place this number in memory. Work out the answer to the top line. Divide by memory recall.

Calculator keys: (look at your calculator instruction booklet if you do not know how to use the memory)

your memory key could say $\boxed{M^{IN}}$

$\boxed{7}$ $\boxed{\cdot}$ $\boxed{2}$ $\boxed{5}$ $\boxed{x}$ $\boxed{3}$ $\boxed{\cdot}$ $\boxed{6}$ $\boxed{8}$ $\boxed{=}$ $\boxed{M}$
$\boxed{3}$ $\boxed{\cdot}$ $\boxed{8}$ $\boxed{6}$ $\boxed{-}$ $\boxed{4}$ $\boxed{\cdot}$ $\boxed{2}$ $\boxed{3}$ $\boxed{=}$ $\boxed{\div}$ $\boxed{MR}$ $\boxed{=}$

Answer –0·013868065

Using a calculator: Powers, roots, memory

Learn to use your calculator to do all of these calculations.

Use of power and root keys

Square key [x^2] This is used to square a number, eg $8^2 = 64$

Power key [x^y] or [y^x] This is used to calculate powers, eg 2^{-3}

Calculator keys: [2][x^y][3][+/-][=] Answer 0·125

Square root [√] This is used to calculate the square root of a number, eg $\sqrt{36} = 6$

Cube root [$\sqrt[3]{}$] This is used to calculate the cube root of a number, eg $\sqrt[3]{125} = 5$

Root key [$\sqrt[x]{}$] or [$x^{\frac{1}{y}}$] This is used to calculate the root of a number, eg $\sqrt[5]{32} = 2$

Calculator keys: [3][2][$x^{\frac{1}{y}}$][5][=] Answer 2

Use of memory

Most calculators use: [M] to put into memory. [MR] is used to recall what is in memory.

If you need to use a number more than once it may help reduce the calculation by saving the number in memory. But remember: When you put a number into memory, you will lose the previous number in memory.

Questions

1 Calculate $8^2 + 5^2$

2 What is the value of 4^5?

3 A square has an area of 81 cm². What is the length of each side?

4 A cube has a volume of 64 cm³. What is the length of each side?

5 $y = 3x^3 + 4x^2 + 2x$. Calculate the value of y when x = 2.974

6 Calculate $\sqrt[4]{16}$

7 Calculate 4^{-2}

Answers

1 Calculator keys [8][x^2][+][5][x^2][=] Answer 89

2 Calculator keys [4][x^y][5][=] Answer 1024

3 Calculator keys [8][1][√] Answer 9 cm

4 Calculator keys [6][4][$\sqrt[3]{}$] Answer 4 cm

5 First put 2.974 into memory. Calculator keys [2][·][9][7][4][M]

   Calculator keys [3][x][MR][x^y][3][+][4][x][MR][x^2][+][2][x][MR][=]

   Answer 120.24

6 Calculator keys [1][6][$x^{\frac{1}{y}}$][4][=] Answer 2

7 Calculator keys [4][x^y][2][+/-][=] Answer 0·0625

Standard form

Standard form is used to write very large and very small numbers.

$5 \cdot 36 \times 10^4$

Means move the decimal point
4 places to the right

$5\,3\,6\,0\,0$ = 53 600

$8 \cdot 31 \times 10^{-3}$

Means move the decimal point
3 places to the left

$0\,0\,0\,8\,3\,1$ = 0·00831

In standard form a number is written in the form
$a \times 10^b$
Where a is a number between 1 and 10 and b is an appropriate power of 10

Using a calculator with numbers in standard form

Use the [EXP] or [EE] key

Example $3 \cdot 82 \times 10^4 \times 4 \cdot 26 \times 10^6$

Calculator keys:

| 3 | . | 8 | 2 | EXP | 4 | x |
| 4 | . | 2 | 6 | EXP | 6 | = |

The calculator display shows
$1 \cdot 62732\,^{11}$
This means $1 \cdot 62732 \times 10^{11}$

Questions

1 Write 8.4×10^3 as an ordinary number

2 Write 3.24×10^{-2} as an ordinary number

3 Write 3820 in standard form

4 Write 0.00236 in standard form

5 $7 \cdot 3 \times 10^8 \div 6 \cdot 4 \times 10^{-7}$

Answers

1 $8\,4\,0\,0$ = 8400

2 $0\,0\,3\,2\,4$ = 0·0324

3 Note: In standard form the decimal point is always after the first whole number.

$3\,8\,2\,0$ The decimal point has moved 3 places to the left.
We write the number in standard form as $3 \cdot 82 \times 10^3$

4 $0 \cdot 0\,0\,2\,3\,6$ The decimal point has moved 3 places to the right.
We write the number in standard form as $2 \cdot 36 \times 10^{-3}$

5    Answer $1 \cdot 140625 \times 10^{15}$

Common error:
Do not put [x][1][0] into your calculator. [EXP] does this.

Another common error is to write $1 \cdot 140625^{15}$.
This will lose marks. You must write $1 \cdot 140625 \times 10^{15}$

Fractions, decimals, percentages and ratio

This section is a lot easier than you think. A variety of methods, including calculator methods, are shown.

Fractions

Fractions are easy if you know how to use your calculator. Make sure your calculator has a fraction key $\boxed{a^b_c}$.

Using a calculator to work out fractions

You need a calculator with a fraction key. It looks like this: $\boxed{a^b_c}$

'Of' means 'Multiply'

Find $^3/_8$ of 43 means $^3/_8$ x 43

Calculator keys: $\boxed{3}$ $\boxed{a^b_c}$ $\boxed{8}$ $\boxed{x}$ $\boxed{4}$ $\boxed{3}$ $\boxed{=}$

The calculator will show | $16 \lrcorner 1 \lrcorner 8$ | This means $16\,^1/_8$

To calculate one number as a fraction of another number

10 people out of 25 went to work by bus. Write this as a fraction in its lowest terms.

Calculator keys: $\boxed{1}$ $\boxed{0}$ $\boxed{a^b_c}$ $\boxed{2}$ $\boxed{5}$ $\boxed{=}$ Answer $^2/_5$

Questions

1. Find $^4/_5$ of 9 $7\,^1/5$ 2. Find $^3/_8$ of £12 $4^1/2$

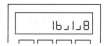

3. 24 pupils out of a class of 36 passed an exam. Write this as a fraction in its lowest terms. $2/3$

4. $2^1/_3$ x $^4/_5$ $1\,^{13}/_{15}$

Answers

1. Calculator keys: $\boxed{4}$ $\boxed{a^b_c}$ $\boxed{5}$ $\boxed{x}$ $\boxed{9}$ $\boxed{=}$

   The calculator will show | $7 \lrcorner 1 \lrcorner 5$ | This means $7\,^1/_5$

2. Of means multiply $^3/_8$ x 12 = £4.50

3. Calculator keys: $\boxed{2}$ $\boxed{4}$ $\boxed{a^b_c}$ $\boxed{3}$ $\boxed{6}$ $\boxed{=}$ Answer $^2/_3$

4. Calculator keys: $\boxed{2}$ $\boxed{a^b_c}$ $\boxed{1}$ $\boxed{a^b_c}$ $\boxed{3}$ $\boxed{x}$ $\boxed{4}$ $\boxed{a^b_c}$ $\boxed{5}$ $\boxed{=}$ Answer $1^{13}/_{15}$

Changing between decimals and percentages

Percent means out of 100. Consequently dividing by 100 will change percentages to decimals, and multiplying by 100 will change decimals to percentages. This page shows you the quick way to change decimals to percentages and percentages to decimals.

Converting percentages to decimals

Move the decimal point two places to the left.

$$38\% \longrightarrow 0\overset{\frown}{38}. = 0.38$$

$$30\% \longrightarrow 0\overset{\frown}{30}. = 0.30 = 0.3$$

$$5\% \longrightarrow 0\overset{\frown}{05}. = 0.05$$

$$27.4\% \longrightarrow 0\overset{\frown}{27}.4 = 0.274$$

Converting decimals to percentages

Move the decimal point two places to the right.

$$0.52 \longrightarrow 0.\overset{\frown}{52} = 52\%$$

$$0.7 \longrightarrow 0.\overset{\frown}{70} = 70\%$$

$$0.03 \longrightarrow 0.\overset{\frown}{03} = 3\%$$

$$0.365 \longrightarrow 0.\overset{\frown}{36}5 = 36.5\%$$

Questions

1. Convert the following percentages to decimals:

   a 74% = 0.74   b 6% = 0.06   c 42.2% = 0.422

2. Change these decimals to percentages:

   a 0.52 = 52%   b 0.08 = 8%   c 0.026 = 2.6%

Answers

1	a	0.74	b	0.06	c	0.422
2	a	52%	b	8%	c	2.6%

Changing between decimals, percentages and fractions

Make sure you understand the previous page then try this page.

Converting percentages to fractions

First convert the percentage to a decimal (see previous page) and then proceed as below.

Converting decimals to fractions

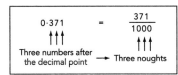

$$0.3 = \frac{3}{10}$$

One number after the decimal point → One nought

$$0.37 = \frac{37}{100}$$

Two numbers after the decimal point → Two noughts

$$0.371 = \frac{371}{1000}$$

Three numbers after the decimal point → Three noughts

$$0.03 = \frac{3}{100}$$

Two numbers after the decimal point → Two noughts

Converting fractions to decimals

Divide the top number by the bottom number.

$^3/_4$	means	$3 \div 4$	=	0.75
$^{17}/_{20}$	means	$17 \div 20$	=	0.85
$^3/_{40}$	means	$3 \div 40$	=	0.075

or with a calculator:

Converting fractions to percentages

First convert the fraction to a decimal (see above), then convert the decimal to a percentage (see previous page).

Questions

1   Convert the following decimals to fractions:

   a 0.4 $= \frac{4}{10}$ b 0.24 $= \frac{24}{100}$

   c 0.02 $= \frac{2}{100}$ d 0.027 $= \frac{27}{1000}$

2   Write these fractions as decimals:

   a $^3/_5$ $= 0.6$ b $^{17}/_{25}$ $= 0.68$ c $^5/_8$ $= 0.625.$

Answers

1   a $^4/_{10} = ^2/_5$ b $^{24}/_{100} = ^6/_{25}$
    c $^2/_{100} = ^1/_{50}$ d $^{27}/_{1000}$

2   a   0.6   b   0.68   c   0.625

Ratio – 1

We use ratio everyday – cooking, using maps, making drinks. You use ratio when you put sugar in coffee, eg two spoons of sugar to one cup of coffee.

Questions

1   This is a recipe for soup for four people:

> 800 ml water
> 2 tomatoes
> 100 g beef
> 8 g salt

How much of each ingredient should you use for:
a two people?
b six people?

Write 8:7 in the ratio 1:n

Make this 1 by dividing both sides by 8

$\frac{8}{8} : \frac{7}{8}$

$1 : \frac{7}{8}$

2   Simplify these ratios:

a 4:18   b   30:45

3   The scale of a map is 1:1 000 000

a The distance between Longton and Hilton is 18 cm on the map. What is the actual distance?

b The distance between Bursley and Higham is 142 km. What is the distance on the map?

4   Write 5:16 in the ration n:1

Answers

1   a   Two people will need half the ingredients: 400 ml water, 1 tomato, 50 g beef and 4 g salt

   b   Six people will need one and a half times the ingredients: 1200 ml water, 3 tomatoes, 150 g beef, 12 g salt

2   a   4:18, divide both sides by 2 ⟶ 2:9

   b   30:45, divide both sides by 15 ⟶ 2:3

3   1:1 000 000 means 1 cm on the map represents 1 000 000 cm on the ground

   1 000 000 cm = 10 000 m = 10 km

   Therefore 1 cm on the map represents 10 km on the ground

   a   18 cm on the map means (18 x 10) km on the ground = 180 km

   b   142 km is represented by (142 ÷ 10) cm on the map = 14.2 cm

4   5:16

        Make this 1 by dividing both sides by 16

     $\frac{5}{16} : \frac{16}{16}$

     $\frac{5}{16} : 1$

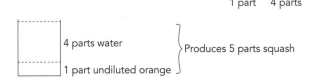

Ratio – 2

Think of ratio as an ordinary everyday bit of Maths.

You use ratio every day of your life. A simple example is making a glass of orange squash. You use undiluted orange and water in the ratio 1 : 4

1 part   4 parts

4 parts water

1 part undiluted orange

} Produces 5 parts squash

How many litres of squash can be made with a three-litre bottle of undiluted orange?

The ratio is	undiluted orange		water		squash
	1	:	4	⟶	5
	one part		four parts		five parts

One part is 3 litres

Therefore five parts is 5 x 3 = 15 litres

Question

A man leaves £5000 in his will. The money is to be divided between his three sons Adam, Ben and Carl in the ratio 2:3:5. How much does each son receive?

Answer

Adam receives	2 parts
Ben receives	3 parts
Carl receives	5 parts
Total	**10 parts**

10 parts is £5000
Therefore 1 part is £500

Adam receives	2 parts	= £1000 (ie 2 x 500)
Ben receives	3 parts	= £1500
Carl receives	5 parts	= £2500

Percentages

This is a very important area of Mathematics.

To calculate one number as a percentage of another number you always **divide**.

Example

284 people out of 800 wore glasses. Write this as a percentage.

> 284 out of 800 means 284 ÷ 800
>
> Then multiply by 100 to find the percentage,
>
> ie 284 ÷ 800 x 100 = 35·5%
>
> An alternative is to use the % key on your calculator

Calculator keys: **2** **8** **4** **÷** **8** **0** **0** **%**   Answer 35.5%

Note: With some calculators you may have to press **INV** or **SHIFT** **%**

With some calculators you may have to press **=** at the end.

Questions

1   A man earns £250 per week. He receives a £4 increase.
     What percentage increase is this?

2   A TV normally costs £400. In a sale this price is reduced to £340. Calculate the
     percentage reduction.

Answers

1   4 ÷ 250 x 100 = 1·6%   or **4** **÷** **2** **5** **0** **%** = 1·6%

2   First calculate the reduction. £400 – £340 = £60
     You always use the original price, ie £400

     60 ÷ 400 x 100 = 15%   or **6** **0** **÷** **4** **0** **0** **%** = 15%

     You always **divide** if you want the answer to be %

Percentages and fractions

You have to be able to work out percentages. Shops often have sales with 20% off. If you cannot do percentages you cannot work out the sale price.

> To find 6%, multiply by 0·06
>
> To calculate a 6% increase, multiply by 1·06 (ie 1 + 0.06)
>
> To calculate a 12% decrease, multiply by 0·88 (ie 1 − 0.12)
>
> To calculate $^2/_3$, multiply by $^2/_3$
>
> To calculate a $^2/_3$ increase, multiply by $1^2/_3$ (ie 1 + $^2/_3$)
>
> To calculate a $^2/_3$ decrease, multiply by $^1/_3$ (ie 1 − $^2/_3$)

Examples

1. A man earns £12 000 per annum. He receives a 4% increase each year. How much does he earn after five years?

   Method: 12 000 x 1·04 x 1·04 x 1·04 x 1·04 x 1·04 = £14 599·83
   A shortcut is: 12 000 x $1·04^5$ = £14 599.83

2. A television costs £200 + 17.5% VAT. What is the total cost?
   200 x 1.175 = £235

> **This is a common examination question:**
>
> A television costs £235 including 17.5% VAT. Calculate the cost before VAT was added.
>
> £235 is 117.5%. We need to find 100%. It is example 2 reversed. 235 ÷ 1.175 = £200

Questions

1. A car is bought for £15 000. It depreciates by 9% each year. How much is it worth after three years? (Give your answer to the nearest £.)

2. Decrease 48 by $^1/_3$ 3. Find 8% of 20

Answers

1. 15 000   x   0·91   x   0·91   x   0·91   =   £11 304

   ↑   ↑   ↑
   to find the   to find the   to find the
   value after   value after   value after
   one year   two years   three years

   The calculation can be shortened   15 000 x $(0·91)^3$
   Calculator keys: [1][5][0][0][0][x][0][.][9][1][x'][3][=]

2. Decrease by $^1/_3$ means multiply by (1 − $^1/_3$) = $^1/_3$ 48 x $^2/_3$ = 32

3. Find 8% means multiply by 0·08 ⟶ 0·08 x 20 = 1·6

Number patterns

In this section you will find some patterns which may help you with your coursework projects. Learn the number patterns, eg square numbers.

Exploring number patterns (the nth term)

Examination questions often give you a pattern of numbers and ask you to describe the pattern. This page will help you to break number patterns.

Example

1 Describe how to find each term in the pattern 5, 8, 11, 14, 17
2 What is the tenth term?

Method

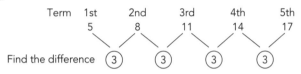

The difference is 3. This is what you multiply by:

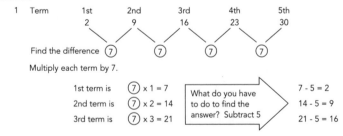

1st term is   ③ x 1 = 3   What do you have to do to find the answer? Add 2   3 + 2 = 5

2nd term is   ③ x 2 = 6   6 + 2 = 8

3rd term is   ③ x 3 = 9   9 + 2 = 11

The rule is multiply the term by 3, then add 2. (In algebraic terms this is 3n + 2.)

The tenth term is 3 x 10 + 2 = 32

Questions

1 Find the rule to produce this pattern: 2, 9, 16, 23, 30
2 What is the 20th term?   c   What is the 362nd term?

Answers

1   Term   1st   2nd   3rd   4th   5th
           2   9   16   23   30

Find the difference ⑦   ⑦   ⑦   ⑦

Multiply each term by 7.

1st term is   ⑦ x 1 = 7   What do you have to do to find the answer? Subtract 5   7 - 5 = 2

2nd term is   ⑦ x 2 = 14   14 - 5 = 9

3rd term is   ⑦ x 3 = 21   21 - 5 = 16

The rule is multiply the term by 7, then subtract 5 (in algebraic terms this is 7n − 5)

2   The 20th term is   7 x 20 − 5 = 135   c   The 362nd term is 7 x 362 − 5 = 2529

Patterns you must recognise

These number patterns often appear in coursework and on examination papers. Life is much easier if you recognise them immediately. Learn these number patterns. They will help you to stay one step ahead of the examiner.

Square numbers

(eg 6 x 6 = 36, therefore 36 is a square number) **Note:** 6 is the square root of 36

□	⊞	⊞	▦	etc					
1,	4,	9,	16,	25,	36,	49,	64,	81,	100

Cube numbers

(eg 5 x 5 x 5 = 125, therefore 125 is a cube number) **Note:** 5 is the cube root of 125

◈	⬡	⬡	⬡	etc					
1,	8,	27,	64,	125,	216,	343,	512,	729,	1000

Triangle numbers

.	∴	∷.	∷∴.	etc					
1,	3,	6,	10,	15,	21,	28,	36,	45,	55
(1)	(1+2)	(1+2+3)	(1+2+3+4)	etc					

Fibonacci sequence

(Add the two previous terms in the sequence).

1,	1,	2,	3,	5,	8,	13,	21,	34,	55
		(1+1=2)	(1+2=3)	(2+3=5)	(3+5=8)	(5+8=13)	etc		

Information you should know

Multiples: The multiples of 3 are 3, 6, 9, 12, 15...
Any number in the 3 times table is a multiple of 3, eg 36, 42, 300.

Factors: The factors of 12 are 1, 2, 3, 4, 6, 12
Any number which divides exactly into 12 is a factor of 12.

Prime numbers: Prime numbers have **exactly two** factors.
The prime numbers are 2, 3, 5, 7, 11, 13, 17, 19...

Note: 1 is not a prime number because it has only one factor.

Product of primes, highest common factor, lowest common multiple and reciprocals

There are many ways of calculating the highest common factor (HCF) and lowest common multiple (LCM). If you have your own method and it works stick with it. If not use the methods below:

Reciprocals

A number multiplied by its reciprocal equals 1.

The reciprocal of $^2/_3$ is $^3/_2$ (ie $^2/_3 \times ^3/_2 = 1$)

To find a reciprocal turn the number upside down, eg reciprocal of $^3/_4$ is $^4/_3$

Reciprocal of -4 is $-^1/_4$ (**Note:** -4 means $-^4/_1$)

Questions

1   Write 1176 as a product of primes

2   Find the HCF and LCM of 1176 and 420

3   What is the reciprocal of 5?

Answers

1   (Remember prime numbers are 2, 3, 5, 7, 11, 13…)

Keep dividing 1176 by the prime numbers, starting with 2, then 3, then 5, etc.

```
2 | 1176
2 |  588
2 |  294
3 |  147  ←——— (2 will not go into 147, so try 3)
7 |   49  ←——— (3 will not go into 49, so try 5)
                (5 will not go into 49, so try 7)
7 |    7
       1  ←——— Note: Keep dividing by prime numbers until you get to 1
```

The prime factors of 1176 are $2 \times 2 \times 2 \times 3 \times 7 \times 7 = 2^3 \times 3 \times 7^2 = 2^3.3.7^2$

Note: the use of the dot is a quicker method of indicating 'multiply'

2   Write 1176 as a product of primes (see above) $2 \times 2 \times 2 \times 3 \times 7 \times 7$

then write 420 as a product of primes $2 \times 2 \times 3 \times 5 \times 7$

HCF (factors in both)	2	x	2			x	3			x	7			= **84**
1176 =	2	x	2	x	2	x	3			x	7	x	7	
420 =	2	x	2			x	3	x	5	x	7			
LCM (maximum number of factors)	2	x	2	x	2	x	3	x	5	x	7	x	7	= **5880**

3   $^1/_5$

Formulae

This is algebra. That's just Maths with letters instead of numbers. It looks harder but the rules are just the same. Spend some time on the example below. Replacing letters with numbers helps your brain understand what is being done and is the 'secret' to algebra. **If you can't do it with letters replace the letters with numbers.** Use easy numbers and avoid using 0 or 1 – strange things happen if you do.

Writing in algebra

Example

Sarah is 5 cm taller than Jayne. Jayne is T cm tall. How tall is Sarah?

If you do not know how to write the answer using symbols, try using numbers instead of the letters,

eg Suppose Jayne is 100 cm tall,   Sarah is 100 + 5
    Suppose Jayne is 120 cm tall,   Sarah is 120 + 5
    Suppose Jayne is 140 cm tall,   Sarah is 140 + 5

Now try letters.
    Suppose Jayne is T cm tall,   Sarah is (T + 5) cm tall

Questions

1   A boy has X pence. He spends Y pence. How much does he have left?

2   A man buys P oranges at Q pence each. What is the total cost?

Answers

1   Try using numbers instead of letters
        Suppose the boy has 30 pence and spends 10 pence   30 – 10
        Suppose the boy has 40 pence and spends 25 pence   40 – 25
        Suppose the boy has 80 pence and spends 30 pence   80 – 30
        Now try letters
        Suppose the boy has X pence and spends Y pence   X – Y

2   Try using numbers instead of letters
        Suppose the man buys 4 oranges at 7 pence each   4 x 7
        Suppose the man buys 6 oranges at 8 pence each   6 x 8
        Suppose the man buys 9 oranges at 3 pence each   9 x 3
        Now try letters
        Suppose the man buys P oranges at Q pence each   P x Q

Using algebra

The more you do algebra, the easier it becomes. The examples below show you the types of questions you can expect to meet.

Examples

Given a = 2, b = 3, c = 4, work out the following:

1   ab   2   abc   3 $^1/_4$ab

4   (a+b)c   5   a(b+c)

Method

1   ab means a x b   2   abc means a x b x c   3 $^1/_4$ab means $^1/_4$ x a x b
         2 x 3   2 x 3 x 4 $^1/_4$ x 2 x 3

     Answer 6   Answer 24   Answer 1·5

4   (a+b)c means (a + b) x c   5   a(b+c) means a x (b + c)
             (2 + 3) x 4   2 x (3 + 4)

Calculator keys: ·   Calculator keys:

$\boxed{(}\,\boxed{2}\,\boxed{+}\,\boxed{3}\,\boxed{)}\,\boxed{x}\,\boxed{4}\,\boxed{=}$ $\boxed{2}\,\boxed{x}\,\boxed{(}\,\boxed{3}\,\boxed{+}\,\boxed{4}\,\boxed{)}\,\boxed{=}$

             Answer 20   Answer 14

Questions

1   A = $^1/_2$BH   Find A when B = 8 and H = 4 $8 \times 4 = 32 \div 2 = \underline{\mathbf{16}}$.

2   P = 2(L+W)   Find P when L = 6 and W = 4 $2 \times 10 = \underline{20}$

3   D = $\dfrac{A+E}{BC}$ Find D when A = 20, B = 2, C = 5 and E = 40 $\dfrac{60}{10} = \mathbf{6}$

Answers

1   A = $^1/_2$ x B x H   2   P = 2 x (L + W)
      = $^1/_2$ x 8 x 4   = 2 x (6 + 4)
      = 16   Calculator keys:

                                              $\boxed{2}\,\boxed{x}\,\boxed{(}\,\boxed{6}\,\boxed{+}\,\boxed{4}\,\boxed{)}\,\boxed{=}$
              A+E   = 20
3   D = ─────
               BC

     = $\dfrac{(20 + 40)}{(2 \times 5)}$ **Note:** Remember the brackets (see page 8)

Calculator keys: $\boxed{(}\,\boxed{2}\,\boxed{0}\,\boxed{+}\,\boxed{4}\,\boxed{0}\,\boxed{)}\,\boxed{\div}\,\boxed{(}\,\boxed{2}\,\boxed{x}\,\boxed{5}\,\boxed{)}\,\boxed{=}$

Answer = 6

I have given you a few basic rules then some examples to show how they work.

Rules

You must know all of these rules. When you do the questions make sure your working is the same as shown in the answers. Don't just say "I can see the answer, I don't need to do any working". Try to get into good habits. You will not be able to just "see the answer" when numbers are difficult. Spend time on this page, it will make *Harder equations* on page 26 easier.

+ is the opposite of –	– is the opposite of +
x is the opposite of ÷	÷ is the opposite of x

Rules for solving equations

1   3a means 3 x a

2   The sign in front of a number is attached to that number,
    eg –3 + 6a. The – is attached to the 3, the + is attached to 6a.

3   Always keep the equals signs in straight columns. Work down the page not across.

4   When you take a number from one side of the equals to the other:

    + becomes –   – becomes +
    x becomes ÷   ÷ becomes x

5   Do the addition and subtraction parts before the multiplication and division.

6   Letters one side, numbers the other (see question 7).

Questions

1   $a + 5 = 8$ 2 $a - 2 = -7$ 3 $-7y = 28$ 4 $y/3 = 6$

5   $5a + 7 = 27$ 6 $a/3 - 5 = 1$ 7 $8a + 6 = 5a - 21$

Answers

1   $a + 5 = 8$
    $a = 8 - 5$
    $a = 3$

2   $a - 2 = -7$
    $a = -7 + 2$
    $a = -5$

3   $-7y = 28$
    $y = 28/_{-7}$
    $y = -4$

4   $y/3 = 6$
    $y = 6 \times 3$
    $y = 18$

5   $5a + 7 = 27$ Deal with the add first
    $5a = 27 - 7$
    $5a = 20$ Now deal with the multiplication
    $a = 20/5$
    $a = 4$

6   $a/3 - 5 = 1$
    $a/3 = 1 + 5$
    $a/3 = 6$
    $a = 6 \times 3$
    $a = 18$
    Keep equals signs in straight columns

7   $8a + 6 = 5a - 21$
    $8a - 5a = -21 - 6$
    $3a = -27$
    $a = -27/_3$
    $a = -9$

Writing equations

Remember 'putting numbers in for letters' helps your brain to understand.

Advice: Look at page 21 *Writing in algebra* before you try this page.

Formulating linear equations

You must understand a problem before you can write an equation to solve it. Try putting numbers in for the letters. This will help you to understand what the question is asking.

Questions

1   A man buys t apples at 8p each. The total cost is 96p.

   a   Form an equation to show this
   b   Solve the equation

2   I think of a number N, I double it and add 15. The answer is 31.

   a   Form an equation to show this
   b   Solve the equation

Answers

1   a   Try putting numbers in for the letters.

        5 apples = 8 x 5 = 40
        6 apples = 8 x 6 = 48
        7 apples = 8 x 7 = 56
        t apples = 8 x t = 96

    The equation is $8t = 96$

   b $8t = 96$

     $t = {}^{96}/_8$

     $t = 12$

2   a   Choose numbers. See what happens:

       if N = 3 $3 \times 2 + 15 = 21$
       if N = 4 $4 \times 2 + 15 = 23$
       if N = 5 $5 \times 2 + 15 = 25$
       Try N $N \times 2 + 15 = 31$

    The equation is $N \times 2 + 15 = 31$ or $2N + 15 = 31$

   b $N \times 2 + 15 = 31$

          $N \times 2 = 31 - 15$

          $N \times 2 = 16$

             $N = {}^{16}/_2$

             $N = 8$

Trial and improvement

This used to be called trial and error. But mathematicians do not like errors so they changed the name to improvement. Make sure you remember the four columns.

WARNING: This topic can be a time-waster in the examination. If you are short of time this is a question to leave and go back to at the end.

Trial and improvement

You should draw four columns as shown below.

In the first column write down your guess.
In the second column work out the answer using your guess.

Advice: Always write the question with the letters on one side, numbers on the other side, eg if the question states solve $x^3 = 2x^2 + 25$ by trial and improvement rewrite the question as $x^3 - 2x^2 = 25$ then proceed as shown in the answer below.

If your answer is too big write your **guess** in the 'too big' column.
If your answer is too small write your **guess** in the 'too small' column.

Guess x	Answer	Too big	Too small

Question

$x^2 + 2x = 39$

Find the value of x correct to one decimal place using trial and improvement methods.

Answer

You must show your working. For example, start by guessing 5. You may have used different guesses in your calculations.

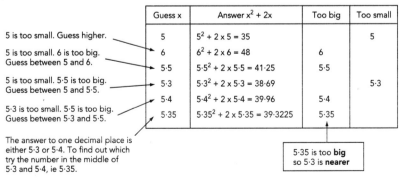

5 is too small. Guess higher.

5 is too small. 6 is too big. Guess between 5 and 6.

5 is too small. 5·5 is too big. Guess between 5 and 5·5.

5·3 is too small. 5·5 is too big. Guess between 5·3 and 5·5.

Guess x	Answer $x^2 + 2x$	Too big	Too small
5	$5^2 + 2 \times 5 = 35$		5
6	$6^2 + 2 \times 6 = 48$	6	
5·5	$5 \cdot 5^2 + 2 \times 5 \cdot 5 = 41 \cdot 25$	5·5	
5·3	$5 \cdot 3^2 + 2 \times 5 \cdot 3 = 38 \cdot 69$		5·3
5·4	$5 \cdot 4^2 + 2 \times 5 \cdot 4 = 39 \cdot 96$	5·4	
5·35	$5 \cdot 35^2 + 2 \times 5 \cdot 35 = 39 \cdot 3225$	5·35	

The answer to one decimal place is either 5·3 or 5·4. To find out which try the number in the middle of 5·3 and 5·4, ie 5·35.

5·35 is too **big** so 5·3 is **nearer**

Answer = 5·3

Harder equations

You may need to refresh your memory. Make sure you remember the rules for solving equations on page 23.

Look at this: $\sqrt{16} = 4$ and $4^2 = 16$

therefore $16 = 4^2$ $4 = \sqrt{16}$

This is how it works in equations: $\sqrt{A} = 6$ and $C^2 = 80$

therefore $A = 6^2$ $C = \sqrt{80}$

$A = 36$ $C = 8.94$ (approx)

(or -8.94)

Note: All numbers have two square roots. One is positive and one is negative, ie $\sqrt{25}$ is $+5$ **or** -5

The following questions show several useful techniques. For each question find the value of y correct to three significant figures where appropriate.

Questions

1   $y^2 = 10$ 2 $\sqrt{y} = 30$ 3 $\sqrt{y} - 3 = 8$

4   $5(y + 3) = 3(4y - 2)$ 5 $6y - 4(2y - 3) = 10$ 6 $\frac{5}{y} + 2 = 6$

Answers

1   $y^2 = 10$ 2 $\sqrt{y} = 30$ 3 $\sqrt{y} - 3 = 8$

$y = \sqrt{10}$ $y = 30^2$ $\sqrt{y} = 8 + 3$

$y = 3.16$ (or -3.16) $y = 900$ $\sqrt{y} = 11$

$y = 11^2$

$y = 121$

4   $5(y + 3) = 3(4y - 2)$ 5 $6y - 4(2y - 3) = 10$ 6 $\frac{5}{y} + 2 = 6$

$5y + 15 = 12y - 6$ $6y - 8y + 12 = 10$ $\frac{5}{y} = 6 - 2$

$5y - 12y = -6 - 15$ $6y - 8y = 10 - 12$ $\frac{5}{y} = 4$

$-7y = -21$ $-2y = -2$ $5 = 4y$

$y = \frac{-21}{-7}$ $y = \frac{-2}{-2}$ $\frac{5}{4} = y$

$y = 3$ $y = 1$ $1.25 = y$

Rewriting formulae

I have shown questions you may be given and the techniques for solving them.
Equations on pages 23 and 26 use the same methods.

Look at this:	$\sqrt{16} = 4$	and	$4^2 = 16$
therefore	$16 = 4^2$		$4 = \sqrt{16}$
This is how it works in formulae:	$\sqrt{C} = D$	and	$E^2 = H$
therefore	$C = D^2$		$E = \sqrt{H}$

The following questions show several useful techniques.
In each question make A the subject.

Questions

1   $\sqrt{A} = B$
2   $A^2 = B$
3   $3C\sqrt{A} = B$

4   $C = B + A$
5   $C = B - A$
6   $C = \dfrac{A}{B}$

7   $C = \dfrac{B}{A}$
8   $AB + C = D$
9   $3B = \dfrac{Y}{2A} - 7$

10   $3B = \dfrac{Y-7}{2A}$
11   $V = \dfrac{1}{3} \pi\, r^2 h$ Make r the subject

Answers

1   $\sqrt{A} = B$
   $A = B^2$

2   $A^2 = B$
   $A = \sqrt{B}$

3   $3C\sqrt{A} = B$

   $\sqrt{A} = \dfrac{B}{3C}$

   $A = \left(\dfrac{B}{3C}\right)^2$

4     $C = B + A$

   $B + A = C$

   $A = C - B$

5     $C = B - A$

   $C + A = B$

   $A = B - C$

6   $C = \dfrac{A}{B}$

   $\dfrac{A}{B} = C$

   $A = BC$

7   $C = \dfrac{B}{A}$

   $AC = B$

   $A = \dfrac{B}{C}$

8   $AB + C = D\,\dot{}$

   $AB = D - C$

   $A = \dfrac{D - C}{B}$

9       $3B = \dfrac{Y}{2A} - 7$

   $3B + 7 = \dfrac{Y}{2A}$

   $A(3B + 7) = \dfrac{Y}{2}$

   $A = \dfrac{Y}{2(3B + 7)}$

10   $3B = \dfrac{Y-7}{2A}$

   $3AB = \dfrac{Y-7}{2}$

   $A = \dfrac{Y-7}{2(3B)}$

   $A = \dfrac{Y-7}{6B}$

11       $V = \dfrac{1}{3} \pi\, r^2 h$

   $3V = \pi\, r^2 h$

   $\left(\dfrac{3V}{\pi h}\right) = r^2$

   $r = \sqrt{\left(\dfrac{3V}{\pi h}\right)}$

Algebraic skills

People tend not to like this section. It is difficult to understand and even more difficult to explain. I have tried to make it as simple as I can.

Using algebraic formulae

Look back at page 22, *Using algebra*. This is similar but harder.

Example

Find D given   a = 3·2   b = 5·4   c = –2·1

$$D = \sqrt{\left(\frac{3a - 2c}{a + c} \right)}$$

Method   First write the question replacing the letters with numbers.

$$D = \sqrt{\left(\frac{3 \times 3\cdot2 - 2 \times \text{-}2\cdot1}{3\cdot2 + \text{-}2\cdot1} \right)}$$

| Look at *Using a calculator* (page 8). |

Work out everything in the brackets.
Remember to put brackets at the start and end of each line.

$$\frac{(3 \times 3\cdot2 - 2 \times \text{-}2\cdot1)}{(3\cdot2 + \text{-}2\cdot1)}$$

Calculator keys:

$$\boxed{(}\ \boxed{3}\ \boxed{x}\ \boxed{3}\ \boxed{\cdot}\ \boxed{2}\ \boxed{-}\ \boxed{2}\ \boxed{x}\ \boxed{2}\ \boxed{\cdot}\ \boxed{1}\ \boxed{+\!/\!-}\ \boxed{)}\ \boxed{\div}$$
$$\boxed{(}\ \boxed{3}\ \boxed{\cdot}\ \boxed{2}\ \boxed{+}\ \boxed{2}\ \boxed{\cdot}\ \boxed{1}\ \boxed{+\!/\!-}\ \boxed{)}$$

Now press $\boxed{=}$ and finally $\boxed{\sqrt{}}$ Answer 3·54...

| **Note:** If you are finding a square root the last two keys will be $\boxed{=}\ \boxed{\sqrt{}}$ |

Question

Calculate the value of r given v = 90, h = 6 and $v = \frac{1}{3} \pi r^2 h$

Answer

First rewrite the formula making r the subject (see question 11 on page 27)

$$r = \sqrt{\left(\frac{3v}{\pi h} \right)} \qquad r = \sqrt{\left(\frac{3 \times 90}{\pi \times 6} \right)}$$

Calculator keys:

$$\boxed{(}\ \boxed{3}\ \boxed{x}\ \boxed{9}\ \boxed{0}\ \boxed{)}\ \boxed{\div}\ \boxed{(}\ \boxed{\pi}\ \boxed{x}\ \boxed{6}\ \boxed{)}\ \boxed{=}\ \boxed{\sqrt{}}$$

Answer 3·78 (approx)

Expansion of brackets

$a^3 \times a^4 = (a \times a \times a) \times (a \times a \times a \times a) = a^7$. Here are some rules to help you.

Indices (powers)

$a^3 \times a^4 = a^7$ If it is multiplication **add** the powers: $3 + 4 = 7$

$a^8 \div a^6 = a^2$ If it is division **subtract** the powers: $8 - 6 = 2$

$(a^5)^3 = a^{15}$ **Multiply** the powers: $5 \times 3 = 15$

$5a^4 \times 3a^6 = 15a^{10}$ **Multiply** the whole numbers and **add** the powers

$8a^3 \div 2a^8 = 4a^{-5}$ **Divide** the whole numbers and **subtract** the powers

Note:	$y^{-3} = \dfrac{1}{y^3}$	$5a^2$ means $5 \times a \times a$ $(5a)^2$ means $5a \times 5a = 25a^2$	$\sqrt[5]{y} = y^{1/5}$

Expansion of brackets

Example: $5y^3(3y^4 + 2ay)$ this means $5y^3 \times 3y^4 + 5y^3 \times 2ay = 15y^7 + 10ay^4$

Questions

1   $3a^5 \times 2a^4 =$ 2 $5a^6 \times 2a =$

3   $3a^2cy^3 \times 4ac^5y^{-5} =$ 4 $12a^3cd^8 \div 3ac^3d^2 =$

Expand the following:

5   $5(2a - 3)$ 6 $3a(5 - 6a)$

7   $4y^6(2y^3 + 4y^2)$ 8 $-3(a^3 + 2y^2)$

9   $4a^3b^2cd^2(3ab^4 - 6ac^3d)$ 10 $(3a + 2)(5a - 3)$

11   $(6a - 7)(4a - 3)$ 12 $(4y - 3)(7y + 6)$

13   $(6a - 4)^2$

Answers

1   $6a^9$

2   $10a^7$ **(Note:** $2a$ means $2a^1$)

3   $12a^3c^6y^{-2}$

4   $4a^2c^{-2}d^6$

5   $5(2a - 3)$
     $10a - 15$

6   $3a(5 - 6a)$
     $15a - 18a^2$

7   $4y^6(2y^3 + 4y^2)$
     $8y^9 + 16y^8$

8   $-3(a^3 + 2y^2)$
     $-3a^3 - 6y^2$

9   $4a^3b^2cd^2(3ab^4 - 6ac^3d)$
     $12a^4b^6cd^2 - 24a^4b^2c^4d^3$

10   $(3a + 2)(5a - 3)$
     $3a(5a - 3) + 2(5a - 3)$
     $15a^2 - 9a + 10a - 6$
     $15a^2 + a - 6$

11   $(6a - 7)(4a - 3)$
     $6a(4a - 3) - 7(4a - 3)$
     $24a^2 - 18a - 28a + 21$
     $24a^2 - 46a + 21$
     Note: $-7 \times -3 = 21$

12   $(4y - 3)(7y + 6)$
     $4y(7y + 6) - 3(7y + 6)$
     $28y^2 + 24y - 21y - 18$
     $28y^2 + 3y - 18$
     Note: $-3 \times 6 = -18$

13   $(6a - 4)^2$
     This means:
     $(6a - 4)(6a - 4)$
     $6a(6a - 4) - 4(6a - 4)$
     $36a^2 - 24a - 24a + 16$
     $36a^2 - 48a + 16$

Factorisation – 1

You must complete the expansion of brackets before factorisation. Factorisation is the reverse operation to expansion of brackets.

Example

Expand   4(2a + 1)   Factorise   8a + 4

           8a + 4   4(2a + 1)

> Factorising means finding common factors
> 6a + 15
>
> 3 is a factor of 6 and 15
> 3(2a + 5)

Questions

Factorise:

1   $30c^2 - 12c = 6c(5c - 2)$ 2 $15c^2d + 20c^5d^4$ $5c^2d(3 + 4c^3 + d^3)$

3   $6a^2bc^3 + 4a^4b^2d$

Answers

1   6 is the highest number that goes into 30 and 12 (ie the highest factor)

   c is the highest power of c that goes into c^2 and c

   6c (5c – 2)

2

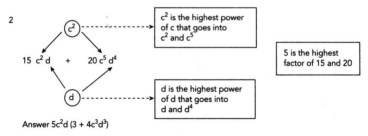

Answer $5c^2d (3 + 4c^3d^3)$

3   2 is the highest number that goes into 6 and 4

   a^2 is the highest power of a that goes into a^2 and a^4

   b is the highest power of b that goes into b and b^2

   $2a^2b(3c^3 + 2a^2bd)$

Factorisation – 2

This page shows the rules when two sets of brackets are required.

Rules for the factorisation of more difficult questions

Look at the last sign.

If the **last** sign is + (positive) then the signs in the brackets will both be the same as the **previous** sign.

If the **last** sign is – (negative) then the signs in the brackets will be **different,** ie one will be + and the other will be –. For example:

Previous sign   Last sign

1   Factorise $x^2 + 5x + 6$ ⟶ $(x + 3)(x + 2)$

2   Factorise $x^2 – 5x + 6$ ⟶ $(x – 3)(x – 2)$

3   Factorise $x^2 + 5x – 6$ ⟶ $(x + 6)(x – 1)$

4   Factorise $x^2 – 5x – 6$ ⟶ $(x – 6)(x + 1)$

Example

Factorise $a^2 – 7a + 10$. Last sign is +, therefore the signs in the brackets will both be the same as the previous sign, ie – (negative).

Multiply these to produce the first term, ie a^2

$$(\quad – \quad)(\quad – \quad)$$

Multiply these to produce the last term, ie 10

The first term: a^2 is produced by multiplying the first term in each bracket. The only possibility is a x a.

The last term: 10 is produced by multiplying the last term in each bracket. Possibilities are 1 x 10, 2 x 5, 5 x 2, 10 x 1.

The middle term: $–7a$ is produced by adding the last term in each bracket,

ie $–1 + –10 = –11$
$–2 + –5 = –7$ ⟶ this works
$–5 + –2 = –7$ ⟶ this works
$–10 + –1 = –11$

Solution: $(a – 2)(a – 5)$ **or** $(a – 5)(a – 2)$

Note: You can check the answer by expanding the brackets (see page 29, question 10). Expanding $(a – 2)(a – 5)$ gives the expression in the question, ie $a^2 – 7a + 10$.

Factorisation – 2 continued

Questions

1 Factorise $y^2 - 2y - 8$

2 Solve $y^2 - 2y - 8 = 0$ by factorisation

Answers

Last sign is negative.

↓

1 $y^2 - 2y - 8$

Therefore the signs in the brackets are different.

$y \times y = y^2$

$(y + \quad)(y - \quad)$ Middle term (ie $-2y$)

+ 1	– 8	⟶	+ 1 – 8 = –7
+ 2	– 4	⟶	**+ 2 – 4 = –2** Correct solution
+ 4	– 2	⟶	+ 4 – 2 = 2
+ 8	– 1	⟶	+ 8 – 1 = 7

Answer $(y + 2)(y - 4)$

2 First factorise (see above)

$(y + 2)(y - 4) = 0$

If two numbers are multiplied together to make 0,
one of the numbers must be 0.

Example: $7 \times \boxed{?} = 0$

↑

This number must be 0.

Remember: $(y + 2)(y - 4)$ means $(y + 2) \times (y - 4)$

If $(y + 2) \times (y - 4) = 0$

then either $y + 2 = 0$ **or** $y - 4 = 0$

                $y = -2$ $y = 4$

Simultaneous equations: Solving using algebra

I know there are quicker ways but here is a method for solving all simultaneous equations. I do not believe in lots of complicated rules and methods. This method will work every time in the same way.

Question

Solve the simultaneous equations: $4x - 5y = 2$
$3x - 2y = 5$

Answer

Make the numbers in front of the 'x' the same.

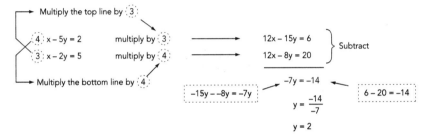

Substitute y = 2 into one of the original equations

$$4x - 5y = 2$$
$$4x - 5 \times 2 = 2$$
$$4x - 10 = 2$$
$$4x = 2 + 10$$
$$4x = 12$$
$$x = 12 \div 4$$
$$x = 3$$

Answer: x = 3, y = 2

Now check by substituting x = 3 and y = 2 in the other original equation	This is just a check.
$3x - 2y = 5$	If you are short of
$3 \times 3 - 2 \times 2 = 5$	time in an exam
$9 - 4 = 5$	you can miss it out.

Sometimes the question is shown like this:

Solve the simultaneous equations $5x = 13 - 2y$ and $3y = 15 - 3x$

First write each question like this:

x terms		y terms	=	number
5x	+	2y	=	13
3x	+	3y	=	15

Now proceed as above.

Graphs

A big section with lots in it.

Drawing lines

Algebra and graphs are closely connected. You must be able to illustrate algebraic information in graphical form.

Graphical representation

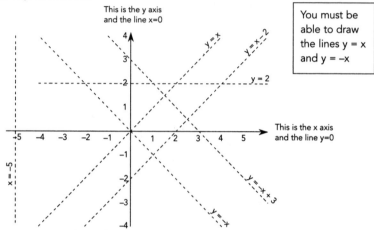

This is the y axis and the line x=0

You must be able to draw the lines y = x and y = −x

This is the x axis and the line y=0

Question

Complete this table of values and draw the graph of $y = -x^2 + 4$

Note: Sometimes the question states draw the function $f(x) = -x^2 + 4$

x	−3	−2	−1	0	1	2	3
y							

Answer

If the question asks for the function $f(x) = -x^2 + 4$ the table and graph will be the same with f(x) instead of y. When x = −3 $y = -(-3)^2 + 4 = -5$

x	−3	−2	−1	0	1	2	3
y	−5	0	3	4	3	0	−5

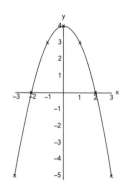

34

Simultaneous equations: Solving by drawing a graph

We solved simultaneous equations by calculation on page 33.
Now we see how to solve them by graphical methods.

Question

Solve the following pair of simultaneous equations by drawing a graph.

$y - 2x = 1$ and $2y - x = 8$

Answer

First draw $y - 2x = 1$

Choose three simple values of x:

eg	When $x = 0$	When $x = 1$	When $x = 3$
	$y - 2x = 1$	$y - 2x = 1$	$y - 2x = 1$
	$y - 2 \times 0 = 1$	$y - 2 \times 1 = 1$	$y - 2 \times 3 = 1$
	$y - 0 = 1$	$y - 2 = 1$	$y - 6 = 1$
	$y = 1$	$y = 1 + 2$	$y = 1 + 6$
		$y = 3$	$y = 7$
	(0,1)	(1,3)	(3,7)

Now draw $2y - x = 8$

Choose three simple values of x:

When $x = 0$	When $x = 1$	When $x = 3$
$2y - x = 8$	$2y - x = 8$	$2y - x = 8$
$2y - 0 = 8$	$2y - 1 = 8$	$2y - 3 = 8$
$2y = 8$	$2y = 8 + 1$	$2y = 8 + 3$
$y = {}^8/_2$	$2y = 9$	$2y = 11$
$y = 4$	$y = {}^9/_2$	$y = {}^{11}/_2$
	$y = 4 \cdot 5$	$y = 5 \cdot 5$
(0,4)	(1,4·5)	(3,5·5)

Plot the values on a graph.
Where the lines cross draw dotted lines.
The solution is $x = 2$, $y = 5$.

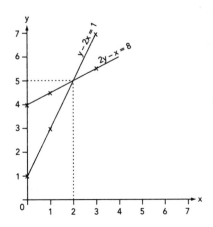

The straight line equation y = mx + c

We can find the equation of a straight line by calculating the gradient and where the line crosses the y-axis. You must learn 'y = mx + c'.

This is the gradient   This is where the line crosses the y axis

$$y = mx + c$$

$$m = \frac{\text{distance up}}{\text{distance across}}$$

If m is negative it is $\dfrac{\text{distance down}}{\text{distance across}}$

Examples

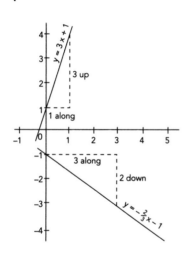

1 $y = \boxed{3}x + \boxed{1}$
     ↓   ↓
     m   c

c = +1   means that the line crosses the y axis at +1

$$m = 3 = \frac{3}{1} \longrightarrow \frac{3 \text{ up the y axis}}{1 \text{ along the x axis}}$$

2 $y = \boxed{-\frac{2}{3}}x \boxed{-1}$
     ↓   ↓
     m   c

c = −1   means that the line crosses the y axis at −1

$$m = -\frac{2}{3} \longrightarrow \frac{2 \text{ down the y axis}}{3 \text{ along the x axis}}$$

Question

What is the equation of the line which passes through the points (1,2) and (3,1)?

Answer

Mark the points (1,2) and (3,1).
Draw a straight line through the points.

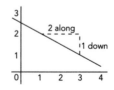

The equation of the line is   y = mx + c
                           $m = -\frac{1}{2}$
                           c = 2.5
                           $y = -\frac{1}{2}x + 2.5$

The line slopes down
The gradient is −ve

Note:

If the line slopes up, the gradient (m) is positive.

If the line slopes down, the gradient (m) is negative.

Drawing graphs

No shortcuts here. You simply have to memorise what the graphs look like.

Graphs

You should recognise these graphs.

Linear graphs   such as $y = 3x + 6$, $y = -\frac{1}{2}x + 2$, etc

   $y = x$ 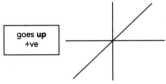 $y = -x$

goes **up** +ve

goes **down** −ve

Quadratic graphs   such as $y = 2x^2 + 3x - 6$, $y = -3x^2 + x + 4$, etc

$y = x^2$ 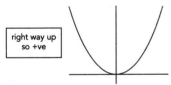 $y = -x^2$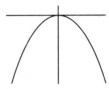

right way up so +ve

upside down so −ve

Cubic graphs   such as $y = x^3 + 2x^2 + x - 1$, $y = -3x^3 + x^2 - 4$, etc

$y = x^3$  $y = -x^3$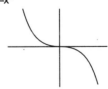

goes **up** +ve

goes **down** −ve

Reciprocal graphs   such as $y = \frac{3}{2x}$, $y = \frac{-4}{x}$, etc

   $y = \frac{1}{x}$ 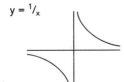 $y = -\frac{1}{x}$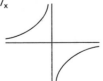

Speed, time and distance graphs

You will be asked to read information from graphs.

This graph shows the journey made
by a car. What is the speed at 0900?

Note: The question may use the
word velocity instead of speed.

> **Note:**
> The gradient gives
> the speed or velocity

Answer:
Speed = 40 km/h

Make this line exactly one hour. Form a right-angled triangle (dotted lines).
The height of the triangle will be the speed in kilometres per hour.

Questions

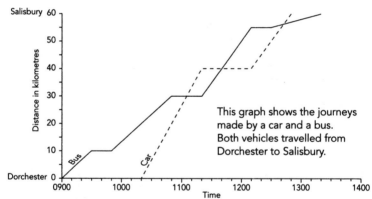

This graph shows the journeys
made by a car and a bus.
Both vehicles travelled from
Dorchester to Salisbury.

1   a   Between which times did the bus travel fastest?
     b   How did you decide?

2   Describe what happened at 11.40.

3   How many times did the car pass the bus?

4   How long did the car stop for?

5   What was the speed of the bus on the first part of its journey?

6   What was the speed of the car at 12.30?

Answers

1   a   11:20 and 12:10   b   The steeper the graph, the faster the bus

2   The bus passed the car   3   twice   4   50 minutes

5   20 km/h   6   30 km/h

Inequalities

Equations have a definite solution, inequalities have a range of solutions. Apart from this they are very similar.

Note: The symbol always points to the smaller number

> means greater than
< means less than
≥ means greater than or equal to
≤ means less than or equal to

Always read the question carefully. Sometimes it asks you to shade the wanted region, sometimes the unwanted region. Sometimes it asks you to describe the shaded region, sometimes the unshaded region.

Questions

1   Solve these inequalities:

a $5x > 20$ b $x - 7 < 10$ c $-2x > 8$
d $3 \leq 2x + 1 < 13$ e $x^2 \geq 16$

2   Draw and indicate the following regions by shading:

a $x > 4$ b $y \leq 2$

Answers

1   Inequalities are very similar to equations:

a $5x > 20$ b $x - 7 < 10$ c $-2x > 8$
   $x > {}^{20}/_5$ $x < 10 + 7$ $x < {}^8/_{-2}$
   $x > 4$ $x < 17$ $x < -4$

Note: When we have a negative multiplication or division the inequality sign reverses. This causes many difficulties. If you are not certain which way the inequality sign should point, try a check. The solution shows x is less than –4. Choose a value less than –4, eg –5:

Is it true that $-2x > 8$?
ie $-2 \times -5 > 8$
              $10 > 8$ Yes, it is true. So $x < -4$ is correct.

d Solve as an equation. $3 \leq 2x + 1 < 13$
   Subtract 1 from everything: $3 - 1 \leq 2x + 1 - 1 < 13 - 1$
                      $2 \leq 2x < 12$
   Divide everything by 2: $1 \leq x < 6$

e Remember, if $x^2 = 16$ then x can equal 4 or –4, ie $4 \times 4 = 16$, $-4 \times -4 = 16$. Therefore $x \geq 4$, $x \leq -4$

2a

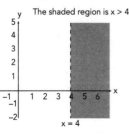

The shaded region is $x > 4$

$x = 4$

Note: We use a dotted line when it is < or >

b

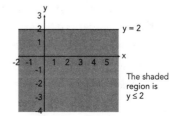

$y = 2$

The shaded region is $y \leq 2$

Note: We use a solid line when it is ≥ or ≤

Angles

Algebra is finished. Actually it gets easier from now on and we are nearly halfway through. Just make sure you can use a protractor (I advise a 360° one) and you know the rules.

Using a protractor

Protractors are used to measure angles. A small circular protractor, diameter 10 cm is the easiest to use.

Measuring and drawing angles

This is a 360° protractor. It is used to measure angles. It is easier to measure large angles with a 360° protractor, than with a semi-circular protractor.

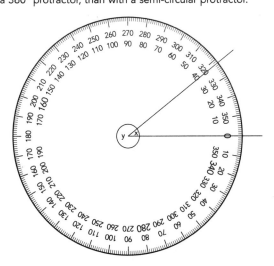

The centre of the protractor must be placed on the point where the two lines meet. You must read the angle very carefully. The angle must be exact. If you are more than 1° away from the exact answer, it is wrong.

Place 0° on the protractor on the line.

Question

Use the protractor drawing above to measure: a angle x and b angle y.

Answer

a   Look at the protractor. There are two numbers at each point. It is obvious that angle x is less than 180°.
    Note: A common mistake is to read the angle as 42°. This is wrong. The angle is between 30° and 40°.
    Angle x = 38°.

b   It is obvious that angle y is more than 180°. Angle y = 322°.

Angles: Acute, obtuse, reflex

You need to know the special names for angles.

Using language associated with angles

An **acute** angle is less than 90°.
These angles are acute.

A **right** angle is 90°.
These are right angles.

We show a right angle with a box in the corner.

An **obtuse** angle is between 90° and 180°.
These angles are obtuse.

There are 180° on a straight line.

180°

A **reflex** angle is between 180° and 360°.
These angles are reflex.

Circles

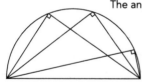

The angle formed in a semi-circle is always 90°.

Note: This is sometimes used in Pythagoras' theorem questions.

The perpendicular bisector of a chord passes through the centre of the circle.

Note: This may be needed for loci questions (see page 71) or trigonometry questions (see page 70).

Perpendicular bisector (ie cuts through the centre of the chord at right angles.)

90°
chord

Note: A chord is a line joining two points on the circumference of a circle.

Intersecting and parallel lines

You need to know the following information about angles. You often need to extend lines to make Z shapes. If you are used to seeing parallel lines going across the page and a question has the lines going down the page it can sometimes help to turn the paper around.

Intersecting lines

$a + b = 180°$
$b + c = 180°$ ⎫ Angles on a straight
$c + d = 180°$ ⎬ line add up to 180°
$d + a = 180°$ ⎭

$a = c$ ⎫ Vertically opposite
$b = d$ ⎬ angles are equal

Parallel lines

Look for ↗Z shapes. Angles at corners of ↗Z↘ shapes are equal.

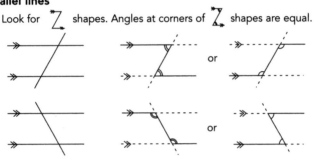

or

or

> Angles at the corners of Z shapes are called **alternate angles**.

> These angles are called **corresponding angles**.

Questions

1 Find the missing angles:

2 Find x:

3 Find y:

Answers

1 a = 140°, b = 40°, c = 140°, d = 40°, e = 140°, f = 40°, g = 140°.

2 It often helps to extend the parallel lines to produce Z shapes.

3 Try adding an extra parallel line

x = 70°

y = 70°

Regular polygons

A polygon is a shape made from straight lines. A regular polygon has all of its sides the same length and all of its angles the same size.

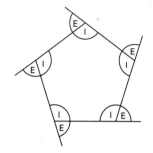

I = Interior angles
E = Exterior angles

The sum of the exterior angles of a polygon is 360°
Interior angle + exterior angle = 180°

Questions

1 Find the size of an exterior and an interior angle of a regular octagon.

2 Find the size of an exterior and an interior angle of a regular hexagon.

Answers

1

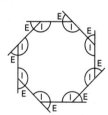

An octagon has 8 sides, 8 exterior angles, 8 interior angles

8 exterior angles°	= 360°
Therefore 1 exterior angle	= $\frac{360}{8}$ = 45°

Interior angle + exterior angle	= 180°
Interior angle + 45°	= 180°
Interior angle	= 135°

2 This question can be solved using the above method.

An alternative method is to split the shape into triangles.

4 triangles are formed
Therefore the sum of the interior angles is

4 x 180°	= 720°

6 interior angles	= 720°
1 interior angle	= 120°

Interior + exterior	= 180°
120° + exterior	= 180°
Exterior	= 60°

Bearings

Bearings are measured clockwise from North. They are easier to measure with a circular protractor (diameter 10 cm). North will usually be shown as vertically up the page. Ensure the 0° on the protractor is on the North line. REMEMBER if the question states "measure the bearing of C from D" you put your protractor on D. Put your protractor on the "from" part of the question.

Questions

1   What is the bearing of A from B?

2   What is the bearing of B from A?

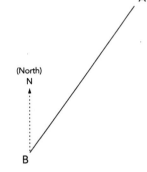

> **Note:** If you know the bearing from A to B, then the bearing from B to A will be 180° more or 180° less, eg:
>
> $$037° + 180° = 217°$$
> $$217° - 180° = 037°$$

Answers

1   Bearings are always measured clockwise from North.
Place your protractor on B. Measure the angle between north and AB.
The angle is 37°.
Bearings are always written as three figures. Answer = 037°

2   Place your protractor on A. Measure the angle. The angle is 217°.
Answer 217°

2-D and 3-D shapes

Most of this section is straightforward. Learn the rules.

2-D representations of 3-D shapes

Most of this is common sense. If you are asked to make an accurate drawing, the drawing must be correct, if any length is more than 1 mm out you will lose marks.

2–D representations of 3–D shapes

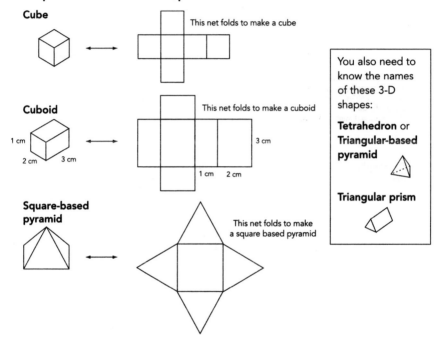

Cube

This net folds to make a cube

Cuboid

This net folds to make a cuboid

1 cm 2 cm 3 cm 3 cm 1 cm 2 cm

Square-based pyramid

This net folds to make a square based pyramid

You also need to know the names of these 3-D shapes:

Tetrahedron or **Triangular-based pyramid**

Triangular prism

Question

Draw an accurate 2-D net of this cuboid.

1 cm 1 cm 2 cm

Answer

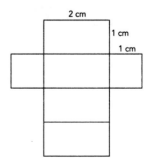

2 cm 1 cm 1 cm

Properties of quadrilaterals

No shortcuts here. You are expected to know these properties. You will have to learn them.

A quadrilateral is a four-sided shape. The angles add up to 360°. You are expected to know the following information about these quadrilaterals.

Parallelogram

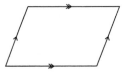

Opposite sides are parallel
and the same length.
Opposite angles are equal.
Diagonals bisect each other.
Rotational symmetry order 2.

Rhombus

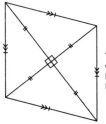

This is a parallelogram
with four equal sides.
Diagonals bisect each other.
Rotational symmetry order 2.

Rectangle

A parallelogram with all angles equal (ie 90°).
Rotational symmetry order 2.

Square

A rectangle with all sides equal length.
Rotational symmetry order 4.

Trapezium

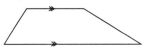

A quadrilateral with one pair of parallel sides.
No rotational symmetry.

Kite

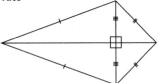

Two pairs of equal length sides
adjacent to each other.
Diagonals cross at right angles.
One diagonal bisects the other.
No rotational symmetry.

Properties of quadrilaterals and triangles

These diagrams show the axes of symmetry.

Rhombus

Rectangle

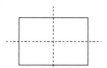

Square

Kite

Parallelogram

Usually none.

Trapezium

Usually none.

You also need to know the special names of these two triangles:

Equilateral

An equilateral triangle has three axes of symmetry. If you fold on any axis of symmetry you produce two identical right-angled triangles.

Isosceles

Two sides equal. Two angles equal.

An isosceles triangle has one axis of symmetry. If you fold on the axis of symmetry you produce two identical right-angled triangles.

Question

This drawing shows two sides of a kite. Complete the drawing.

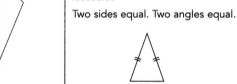

Answer

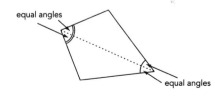

equal angles

equal angles

Similarity

This usually appears on the exam paper. Just recognise the shapes, put them the same way round, then find the scale factor (ie the relationship between the sizes of the shapes).

Similarity

An easy method is shown below.

Two triangles are similar if the angles of one triangle are equal to the angles of the other triangle, eg:

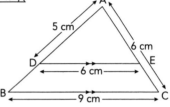

Question

Find the length of AB and AE.

Answer

DE is parallel to BC. Therefore ADE is similar to ABC.

1   Draw the two triangles separately.

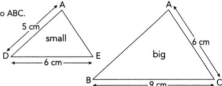

2   Identify the big triangle and the small triangle.

3   Find two sides with lengths given which are in the same position on each triangle. In this example DE and BC.
    DE = 6 cm,   BC = 9 cm

4   The scale factor (SF) from small to big is $\frac{9}{6}$ ie $\frac{big}{small}$.
    To convert any length on the small triangle to a length on the large triangle, multiply by SF $\frac{9}{6}$.
    eg   AD (small triangle) x SF $\frac{9}{6}$ = AB
          5 cm x $\frac{9}{6}$ = 7.5 cm

5   The scale factor from big to small is $\frac{6}{9}$ ie $\frac{small}{big}$.
    To convert any length on the large triangle to a length on the small triangle, multiply by SF $\frac{6}{9}$.
    eg   AC (large triangle) x SF $\frac{6}{9}$ = AE
          6 cm x $\frac{6}{9}$ = 4 cm

Congruency: If two shapes are congruent then they are identical. The angles of one shape are equal to the angles of the other shape **and** the sides of one shape are equal to the sides of the other shape.

Symmetry

There are two types of symmetry: rotational symmetry produced by turning, and symmetry produced by folding to make mirror images.

Rotational symmetry

A shape has rotational symmetry if it fits exactly onto its original outline more than once in a complete turn. The number of times that it fits is called the order of rotational symmetry. If a shape only fits onto itself once we say that it has no rotational symmetry, or that it has order 1.

Shape	Name	Order of rotational symmetry
a	a Square	4
b	b Rectangle	2
c	c Equilateral triangle	3
d	d Regular pentagon	5
e	e Regular hexagon	6

X marks the centre of rotation.

To find the centre of rotation: If a shape has an even number of sides, join opposite corners. If a shape has an odd number of sides, join each corner to the centre of the opposite side.

Question

What is the order of rotational symmetry of this regular octagon?

Mark the centre of rotational symmetry.

Answer

Make a tracing of the octagon. Turn the tracing through one complete turn, ie 360°. It fits the original octagon exactly 8 times. Therefore the order of rotational symmetry is 8.

Symmetry of 2-D shapes

Axes of symmetry

If you fold a shape along an axis of symmetry, the shape will fit exactly onto itself.
If the shape is a regular shape, all sides are equal, all angles are equal. Here are some regular shapes – the dotted lines indicate axes of symmetry.

	Name	Number of sides	Axes of symmetry
	Equilateral triangle	3	3
	Square	4	4
	Regular pentagon	5	5
	Regular hexagon	6	6
	Regular octagon	8	8

Note: If the shape is regular
        number of sides = number of axes of symmetry

Symmetry of 2-D shapes continued

Questions

Here are some common 2–D shapes. Use dotted lines to indicate axes of symmetry.
Give the names of the shapes if you can.

1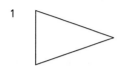

2

3

4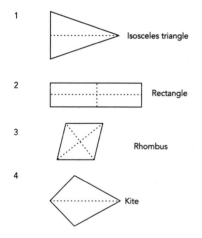

Answers

1 Isosceles triangle

2 Rectangle

A common error is

These are **not** axes of symmetry.

3 Rhombus

4 Kite

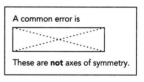

Note: There is only one axis of symmetry on the kite.

Transformations

The main types of transformation are:

Translation – slide the shape left, right, up or down.
Rotation – turn it around.
Reflection – mirror image, ie turn it over.
Enlargement – make it bigger (or smaller).

Enlargement

Enlargement means making bigger or smaller. There are several methods of enlarging. The advantage of the method shown is that it can be used for enlargement by a whole number scale factor and a fractional scale factor.

Questions

1 Enlarge the triangle ABC by a scale factor of 2.

   Centre of this enlargement is the point (2,1).

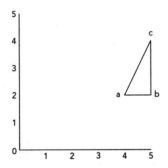

2 R′ is an enlargement of R.
   a What are the co-ordinates of the centre of enlargement?
   b What is the scale factor of the enlargement?

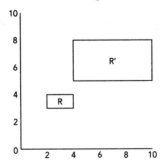

Enlargement continued

1

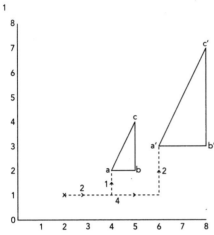

Count the distance from the centre of enlargement to each point

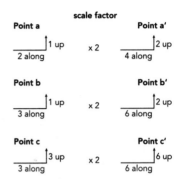

scale factor

Point a

$\lceil$1 up

2 along   × 2

Point a'

$\lceil$2 up

4 along

Point b

$\lceil$1 up

3 along   × 2

Point b'

$\lceil$2 up

6 along

Point c

$\lceil$3 up

3 along   × 2

Point c'

$\lceil$6 up

6 along

Note: Always count from the centre of enlargement.

2

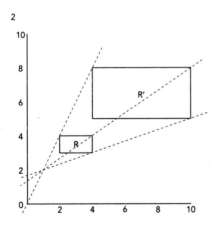

a   Use a ruler to join the corners. The dotted lines cross at (1,2). Therefore the centre of enlargement is the point (1,2)

To find the scale factor, you must measure the length of any side of R' (ie the new length) and the corresponding length of R (ie the original length).

Example:
The top side of R' has a length of 6
The top side of R has a length of 2

b   Scale factor = $\dfrac{\text{new length}}{\text{original length}}$

Scale factor = $\dfrac{6}{2} = 3$

Enlargement by a fractional scale factor

The method of enlargement used here is almost identical to that on pages 52 and 53.

Question

Enlarge the triangle by a scale factor of $^2/_3$. Centre of enlargement is the point (1,1).

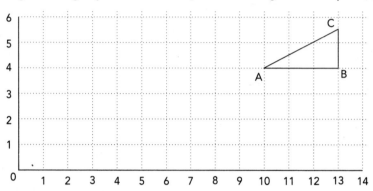

Answer

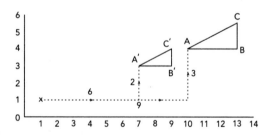

Count the distance from the centre of enlargement to each point.

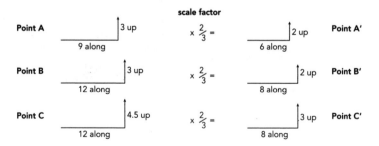

Translations

This is just moving a shape left or right, up or down.

$\binom{3}{4}$ is a vector. The top number means move left or right.
The bottom number means move up or down.

> If the top number is positive it means move right
> If the top number is negative it means move left

> If the bottom number is positive it means move up
> If the bottom number is negative it means move down

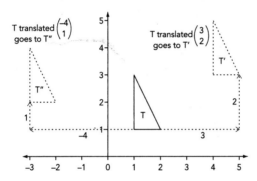

Question

Translate R by the vector $\binom{1}{-5}$. Label this R'

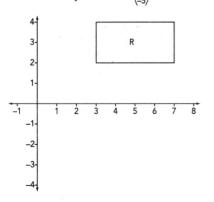

Answer

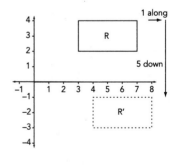

Measurement

Quite a lot to memorise if you don't already know it. Most of this section is everyday Maths. Nothing difficult.

Rough metric equivalents of Imperial units

Imperial units are the old units we used to use before the metric system. Your parents probably still use feet, inches, pounds and stones. Until people stop using Imperial units you have to understand both.

You should know the following information:

Imperial units

Units of length
1 inch is about 2.5 centimetres
1 foot is about 30 centimetres
1 yard is about 1 metre
5 miles are about 8 kilometres

12 inches = 1 foot
3 feet = 1 yard

Units of mass
1 ounce is about 30 grams
2 pounds are about 1 kilogram

16 ounces = 1 pound
14 pounds = 1 stone

Units of capacity
1 pint is about 0.5 litre
1 gallon is about 4.5 litres

8 pints = 1 gallon

Questions

1. My pencil is 8 inches long. How many centimetres is this?

2. My car's petrol tank holds 10 gallons. How many litres is this?

3. A newborn baby weighs 7 pounds. How many ounces is this?

Answers

The following are approximate.

1. 8 x 2.5 = 20 centimetres
2. 10 x 4.5 = 45 litres
3. 7 x 16 = 112 ounces

Converting one metric unit to another

Metric units are easy to convert, you always multiply or divide by 10, 100 or 1000.
Look back at page 3 *Mental arithmetic shortcuts – 2.*

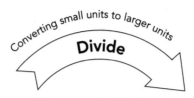

Converting small units to larger units
Divide

You must learn this information {

Length
10 millimetres (mm) = 1 centimetre (cm)
100 centimetres (cm) = 1 metre (m)
1000 metres (m) = 1 kilometre (km)

Mass
1000 grams (g) = 1 kilogram (kg)
1000 kilograms (kg) = 1 tonne (t)

Capacity
1000 cubic centimetres (cc) = 1 litre (l)
1000 millilitres (ml) = 1 litre (l)
100 centilitres (cl) = 1 litre (l)
10 millilitres (ml) = 1 centilitre (cl)

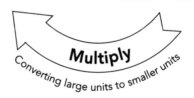

Multiply
Converting large units to smaller units

Questions

1. Convert 524 centimetres into metres
2. Convert 3.56 tonnes into kilograms

Note: 1 cm^3 = 1 cc = 1 ml

Answers

1. 524 ÷ 100 = 5.24 metres
2. 3.56 x 1000 = 3560 kilograms

Measurement

Making sensible estimates

Estimate simply means guess, but your guess has to be sensible. Often you will have to estimate because you do not have enough time to work out the exact answer.

You will often be asked to make sensible estimates of length, mass and capacity. The easiest way to do this is to know the length, mass and capacity of some common objects.

Guess the answers to the following and write your guess in pencil. Then measure the exact answers and write them in the box.

	guess	**exact**

Length

1   My finger is _____ centimetres long.

2   My pace is _____ centimetres long.

3   My classroom is _____ metres long.

4   1 kilometre is the distance from _____ to _____ .

Mass

5   My pencil weighs _____ grams.

6   I weigh _____ kilograms.

7   A Mini car weighs _____ tonne.

Capacity

8   A can of cola holds _____ millilitres.

9   A giant bottle of cola holds _____ litres.

Answers

(Your answers will probably be within these ranges.)

1	5–10 centimetres	2	70–100 centimetres
3	3–8 metres	4	Try walking for 10 minutes. This distance will be about 1 kilometre.
5	5–10 grams	6	40–100 kilograms
7	1 tonne	8	Approximately 330 millilitres – read the label to check
9	Probably 3 litres – read the label to check		

You will need to give units to a sensible degree of accuracy. Try these:

Questions

1   Which unit would you use to measure the distance from London to Manchester?

2   The speed of a car is 76·8327 km/h. Write this to a sensible degree of accuracy.

Answers

1	kilometres	2	77 km/h or 76·8 km/h

Accuracy of measurement

If we count objects or people (ie discrete data) we can get an exact number. If we take a measurement of length, mass, capacity or time (continuous data) the measurement may not be exact. Lengths are often given to the nearest centimetre. This means a possible error of half a centimetre in either direction.

Example

If the length of a desk is given as 1.3 m, this indicates that the length is approximately 1.3 m. The measurement may be inaccurate.

To calculate the minimum possible value:

1·3 ⟶ (Reduce the last digit by 1) ⟶ 1·2 ⟶ (Add a 5) ⟶ **1·25 m**

To calculate the maximum possible value:

1·3 ─────────────────────⟶ (Add a 5) ⟶ **1·35 m**

Therefore if the length is given as 1.3 m, this means the actual length lies between 1.25 m and 1.35 m inclusive.

Questions

1   A book has a mass of 2.18 kilograms. What are the minimum and maximum possible masses of the book?

2   The length of a blackboard is given as 2.80 m. What are the minimum and maximum possible lengths of the blackboard?

3   The length of a room is given as 7 m, correct to the nearest 0·5 m. What are the minimum and maximum possible lengths?

4   Which is more accurate: 6·2 m or 6·20 m? Explain your answer.

Answers

1   Minimum value   2·18 ⟶ (Reduce the last digit by 1) ⟶ 2·17 ⟶ (Add a 5) ⟶ **2·175 kg**

Maximum value   2·18 ─────────────────⟶ (Add a 5) ⟶ **2·185 kg**

2   Minimum value   2·80 ⟶ (Reduce the last digit by 1) ⟶ 2·79 ⟶ (Add a 5) ⟶ **2·795 m**

Maximum value   2·80 ─────────────────⟶ (Add a 5) ⟶ **2·805 m**

3   This question is slightly different. It gives you the level of accuracy, ie 0·5 m.
   Method: Halve the level of accuracy, ie half of 0·5 m is 0·25 m.
   Minimum length is 7 m – 0·25 m = 6·75 m
   Maximum length is 7 m + 0·25 m = 7·25 m

4   6·2 m is correct to one decimal place, 6·20 m is correct to two decimal places. 6·20 is more accurate.

Compound measures

Speed and density are compound measures because we give the speed in m/s or km/h, ie two units. If mass is given in kg and volume in m^3, the density will be given in kg/m^3.

The following formulae must be memorised:

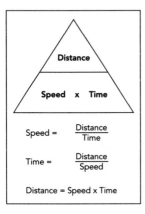

$$Speed = \frac{Distance}{Time}$$

$$Time = \frac{Distance}{Speed}$$

Distance = Speed x Time

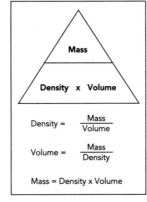

$$Density = \frac{Mass}{Volume}$$

$$Volume = \frac{Mass}{Density}$$

Mass = Density x Volume

You may have used these formulae in Science.

Suppose you want to know what speed equals. Cover up speed. This shows:

Therefore Speed = $\frac{Distance}{Time}$

You will use this method in trigonometry (that is sin, cos, tan) on page 68.

Questions

1   A car takes 8 hours 10 minutes to travel 343 kilometres. Calculate the average speed.

2   A man walks at a speed of 24 metres in 10 seconds. Calculate his speed in kilometres per hour.

3   Mass is given in g, volume is given in cm^3. What units are used for density?

Answers

1   Decide if you require the answer in kilometres per hour or kilometres per minute.

If you choose kilometres per hour change 8 hours 10 minutes into hours.

10 minutes is $^{10}/_{60}$ of an hour.

Therefore 8 hours 10 minutes = $8^{10}/_{60}$ hours.

Speed = $\frac{Distance}{Time}$ = $\frac{343}{8^{10}/_{60}}$ = 42 kilometres per hour.

2   24 metres in 10 seconds

(multiply by 6)	144 metres in 1 minute
(multiply by 60)	8640 metres in 60 minutes (ie 1 hour)
(divide by 1000)	8.64 kilometres in 1 hour
	The speed is 8.64 kilometres per hour.

3   g/cm^3

Time

Your examination paper will contain a time question. We use time frequently so it should be easy. WARNING: At least half of the examination candidates will get the question wrong. Treat the question with respect. Remember there are 60 minutes in an hour NOT 10 or 100; lots of candidates will make this mistake.

A common error is to think 3·5 hours equals 3 hours 50 minutes. It does not. It equals 3 hours 30 minutes. Your calculator will change hours (as a decimal) into hours minutes and seconds. (**Note:** You can only use this method if your calculator has these keys.)

Find the [D°M'S''] key or [° ' ''] or ['' ''] .

These are very useful keys.

Put 3·5 into your calculator and press the [D°M'S''] key or you may have to press the top left key on your calculator (ie [shift] or [INV] or [2nd] followed by [° ' ''] or ['' ''] .

You should get 3°30'00·00 or 3°30'0 this means 3 hours 30 minutes.

Questions

1   A train leaves London at 07:42 and arrives in Glasgow at 13:16. How long does the journey take?

2   A car travels 378 km at 67·9 km/h. How long does the journey take? Give your answer to the nearest second.

You must know:

60 seconds = 1 minute
60 minutes = 1 hour
24 hours   = 1 day
365 days   = 1 year

Answers

1   If you have 5 hours 34 minutes, stick with your own method.

If you obtained the answer 5 hours 74 minutes or 6 hours 14 minutes you have fallen straight into the trap and must study the solution carefully.

		Hours	Minutes
First find the time to the next whole hour.	07:42 to 08:00		18
Now the hours	08:00 to 13:00	5	
Now the minutes	13:00 to 13:16		16
		5 hours	34 minutes

2   Time = $\dfrac{\text{Distance}}{\text{Speed}}$ (see page 60).

$\dfrac{378}{67·9}$ = 5·567010309   **Note:** This does **not** mean 5 hours 56 minutes or 5 hours 57 minutes.
Use the [D°M'S''] or ['' ''] key to change your answer = 5 hours 34 minutes 1 second.

Circles

You are advised to memorise the formulae for circles.

Formulae

You must know how to use all of the formulae shown. Carefully note the two common errors at the bottom of the page.

Circumference of a circle = $2\pi r$
(this means 2 x π x radius)

Area of a circle = πr^2
(this means π x radius x radius)

Volume of a cylinder = $\pi r^2 h$
(this means π x radius x radius x height)

cylinder

A common error: Always ask yourself, does the question give the **radius** or the **diameter**? In any examination about 20% of the candidates will confuse radius and diameter. Be careful you are not one of them. To avoid this, before using any circle formulae ask "Do we have the radius?". If the answer is "Yes", continue. If not, find the radius. The **radius** is **half** of the **diameter**.

Questions

1. Find the circumference and area of a circle radius 6 cm
2. Find the circumference and area of a circle diameter 8 cm
3. Find the radius of a circle, area 40 m^2
4. Find the volume of a cylinder diameter 80 cm, height 1·2 m

Answers

1. Do we have the radius? Yes. Continue.

Circumference = 2 x π x radius	Area = π x radius x radius
= 2 x π x 6	= π x 6 x 6
= 37·7 cm	= 113 cm^2

2. Do we have the radius? No. First we have to find the radius. The radius is 4 cm.

Circumference = 2 x π x radius	Area = π x radius x radius
= 2 x π x 4	= π x 4 x 4
= 25·1 cm	= 50·3 cm^2

3. A = πr^2 (look back to *Rewriting formulae* page 27).
Make r the subject:

$$\frac{A}{\pi} = r^2$$

$$\sqrt{\left(\frac{A}{\pi}\right)} = r$$

$$\sqrt{\left(\frac{40}{\pi}\right)} = r \quad \text{Calculator keys:}$$

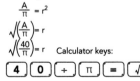

3·57 m = r

> **Question 4 alternative answer**
> If you want the answer in m^3 you **must** convert to metres **before** you multiply:
> = π x 0·4 m x 0·4 m x 1·2 m
> = 0·603 m^3

> **Common error: Never** try to convert squared or cubed units. **Look:**
> 603000 cm^3 does **not** equal 6030 m^3
> Remember this for pages 63 and 64.

4. Do we have the radius? No. First halve the diameter to find the radius. The radius is 40 cm.

Volume = π x radius x radius x height
= π x 40 x 40 x 120
= 603186 cm^3
= 603000 cm^3

> **Common error:** you cannot use mixed units, ie cm and m. Change 1·2 m into 120 cm

Perimeter, area and volume

Fairly straightforward. They give you the formulae on the exam paper so that makes it easier.

Calculating length, area and volume – 1

You need to understand length, area, volume, perimeter and know the units each is measured in. You must know what is meant by cross-section, prism, parallelogram, trapezium, and how to use the formulae. (These formulae will be given on the examination paper.)

> **Remember:** Perimeter is the distance around a shape.
> Area is length x width (always measured in units², eg mm², cm², m²)
> Volume is length x width x height (always measured in units³, eg mm³, cm³, m³)

You are expected to know how to use these formulae:

Area of a triangle
= $^1/_2$ x base x perpendicular height (P.H.)

Area of a parallelogram
= base x perpendicular height

Area of a trapezium
= $^1/_2$ (a + b) x perpendicular height

Volume of a cuboid
= length x width x height

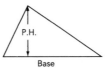

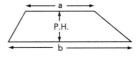

Questions

1   Find **a)** the perimeter; and
       b) the area of this shape.

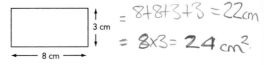

$= 8+8+3+3 = 22cm$

$= 8 \times 3 = 24 \, cm^2$

2   Find the area.

$= 42 \div 2 = 21 cm^2$

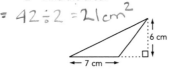

3   Find the area.

$12 \times 5 =$
60 cm²

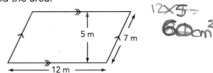

4   Find the area.

$20 + 12 = 32$
$32 \times 8 = 256$
$256 \div 2 = 128$
$= 128 cm^2$

5   Find the volume.

$= 60m^3$

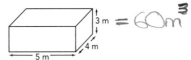

Answers

1   a   8 cm + 3 cm + 8 cm + 3 cm = 22 cm   b   8 cm x 3 cm = 24 cm²

2   $^1/_2$ x 7 cm x 6 cm = 21 cm²   3   12 m x 5 m = 60 m² **(Note:** 7m is not used)

4   Area = $^1/_2$ x (12 cm + 20 cm) x 8 cm   5   5 m x 4 m x 3 m = 60 m³
       = $^1/_2$ x 32 cm x 8 cm
       = 128 cm² **(Common error:** 128 cm² does **not** equal 1·28 m²)

Calculating length, area and volume – 2

Prism

Any solid shape with uniform cross-section, ie same shape at each end.

Cross-section

This is the shape that goes all through a prism, ie the shaded parts in these shapes.

Example

Find the volume of this prism:

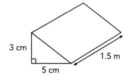

Volume = cross–sectional area x length

First find the cross–sectional area

Area of a triangle = $\frac{1}{2}$ base x height = $\frac{1}{2}$ x 5 x 3 = 7.5 cm^2

Note: The length is 1.5 m. This must be changed into centimetres, ie 150 cm.

Volume = 7.5 cm^2 x 150 cm = 1125 cm^3

Question

Find the area and perimeter of this shape:

Answer

The formula to find the area of a trapezium is $\frac{1}{2}$ (a+b) x perpendicular height.

Area = $\frac{1}{2}$ (4 + 10) x 6

   = $\frac{1}{2}$ (14) x 6

   = 7 x 6

   = 42 cm^2

To find the perimeter we must use Pythagoras' theorem to find the missing side (see *Pythagoras' theorem*, page 67).

$x^2 = 6^2 + 6^2$

$x^2 = 36 + 36$

$x^2 = 72$

$x = \sqrt{72}$

$x = 8.49$ cm

Perimeter = 4 + 6 + 10 + 8.49 = 28.49 cm

Calculating length, area and volume – 3

Volume of a cuboid = length x width x height

Volume of a cuboid = 6 cm x 3 cm x 4 cm

$\qquad\qquad\qquad$ = 72 cm^3

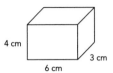

Note: Area is in units^2, eg cm^2, m^2
$\qquad$ Volume is in units^3, eg cm^3, m^3

Questions

1   a   Find the area.
     b   Find the perimeter.

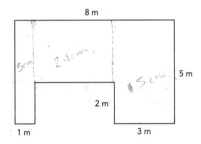

2   This is a diagram of a garden with a lawn and a path around the edge. The path is 2 m wide.

Find the area of the path.

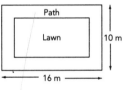

Answers

1   a   Split the shape into three parts.

$\qquad\qquad$ Area = 32 m^2

     b   8 m + 5 m + 3 m + 2 m

$\qquad\qquad$ + 4 m + 2 m + 1 m + 5 m = 30 m

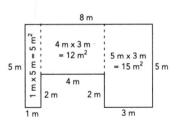

2   Find the area of the large rectangle = 10 x 16   = 160 m^2

    Find the area of the small rectangle = 6 x 12   = 72 m^2

    Take away   = 88 m^2

Note: It is 6 x 12
A common error is 8 x 14.
Remember 2 m wide at both ends

Formulae for length, area and volume

You need to recognise formulae. Which ones are 1-D (length), 2-D (area) and 3-D (volume)?

Length has 1 dimension
Area has 2 dimensions
Volume has 3 dimensions

——————————— 1-D

Length x length = area
Length x length x length = volume
Length x area = volume

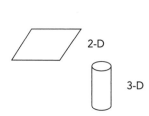

2-D

Length + length = length
Area + area = area
Volume + volume = volume

3-D

Different dimensions cannot be added. For example:

Length cannot be added to area
Volume cannot be added to area
Length cannot be added to volume

Numbers, eg 3, 7, π have no effect on the dimensions. For example:
   r = radius
   r is a length $2\pi r$ is a length
   r^2 is an area πr^2 is an area

> **Note:** Perimeter, radius and diameter are all lengths

Questions

a, b, c and d are lengths.

State whether each formula gives a length, area, volume or none of these.

1   $3ab$

2   $\dfrac{bcd}{3a}$

3   $ab^2 + 3cd^2$

4   $ab + d$

Answers

1   length x length = area
    Answer   area

2   $\dfrac{bcd}{3a} = \dfrac{\text{length x length x length}}{\text{length}} = \dfrac{\text{volume}}{\text{length}}$
    Answer   area

3                  $ab^2 + 3cd^2$
    length x length x length + length x length x length
                volume + volume

    Answer   volume

4                  $ab + d$
    length x length + length
        area   + length

    area cannot be added to length
    Answer   none of these

Pythagoras' theorem and trigonometry

Fairly straightforward. They give you the formulae on the exam paper so that makes it easier.

Pythagoras' theorem

When you know the lengths of two sides of a right-angled triangle you can use Pythagoras' theorem to find the third side.

Pythagoras' theorem: $a^2 + b^2 = c^2$ (where c is the longest side)

Note: The longest side is always opposite the right angle.

Examples

Find x

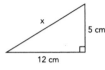

$$5^2 + 12^2 = x^2$$
$$25 + 144 = x^2$$
$$169 = x^2$$
$$\sqrt{169} = x$$
$$13 \text{ cm} = x$$

Find y

$$y^2 + 8^2 = 10^2$$
$$y^2 = 10^2 - 8^2$$
$$y^2 = 100 - 64$$
$$y^2 = 36$$
$$y = \sqrt{36}$$
$$y = 6 \text{ cm}$$

To find the **long** side	To find either **short** side
Square both numbers **Add** them together Take square root of result	Square both numbers **Subtract** the smaller from the larger Take square root of result

Question

1 Find x

2 Find the height of this isosceles triangle:

Answer

1 To find a short side:

Square both numbers 12^2 7^2

Subtract $144 - 49$

(**Note:** Big number – small number. If you do it the wrong way you will get "error" when you press 〔√〕)

Square root $\sqrt{95}$

Answer x = 9·75 m

2 An isosceles triangle can be split into two right-angled triangles.

$$h^2 + 4^2 = 10^2$$
$$h^2 = 10^2 - 4^2$$
$$h^2 = 100 - 16$$
$$h^2 = 84$$
$$h = \sqrt{84}$$
$$h = 9.165 \text{ cm}$$

Trigonometry: Finding an angle

This is finding sides and angles. Remember the rules shown. If you are finding an angle you press the TOP LEFT key on your calculator (ie [shift] [INV] or [2nd F] . If you are finding a side you do **not** press the TOP LEFT key on your calculator.

Information similar to this will be given on your examination paper.

Note: This only works for right-angled triangles.

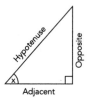

$$SIN = \frac{OPP}{HYP}$$

$$COS = \frac{ADJ}{HYP}$$

$$TAN = \frac{OPP}{ADJ}$$

To find an angle

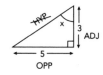

Method

1   Label the triangle
    Hypotenuse = the longest side, opposite the right angle
    Opposite = opposite the angle being used
    Adjacent = next to the angle being used

2   Cross out the side not being used.
    In this question HYP.

3   Look at the formulae in the box at the top. Which uses OPP and ADJ?

4   $TAN = \frac{OPP}{ADJ} = \frac{5}{3}$

5   Calculator keys

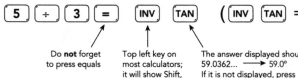

Do **not** forget to press equals

Top left key on most calculators; it will show Shift, Inv or 2nd Function

The answer displayed should be 59.0362... ⟶ 59.0°
If it is not displayed, press [=]

Question

Find x

Answer

$COS = \frac{ADJ}{HYP} = \frac{3}{8}$

$= 67.975687... \longrightarrow 68.0°$

Trigonometry: Finding a side

We have used this method before (see page 60).

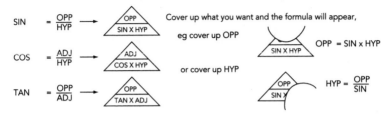

SIN $= \dfrac{OPP}{HYP}$

COS $= \dfrac{ADJ}{HYP}$

TAN $= \dfrac{OPP}{ADJ}$

Cover up what you want and the formula will appear,

eg cover up OPP

OPP = SIN x HYP

or cover up HYP

HYP $= \dfrac{OPP}{SIN}$

To find a side

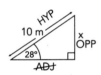

Method

1 Label the triangle
   Hypotenuse = the longest side, opposite the right angle
   Opposite = opposite the angle being used
   Adjacent = next to the angle being used

2 You need the side you are finding (x).
   You need the side you know (10 m).
   Cross out the side not being used. In this question ADJ.

3 Look at the formulae above. Which uses OPP and HYP?

4 We need OPP, cover up OPP to find the formula:

OPP = SIN x HYP
OPP = SIN28° x 10

5 Calculator keys

This should give you an answer 4.6947.. ⟶ 4.69 m

Note: If this does not work ask your teacher to show you how to work your calculator.

Question   Answer

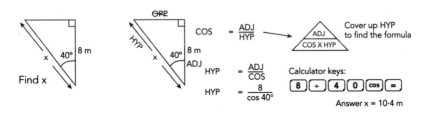

Find x

COS $= \dfrac{ADJ}{HYP}$

HYP $= \dfrac{ADJ}{COS}$

HYP $= \dfrac{8}{\cos 40°}$

Cover up HYP
to find the formula

Calculator keys:

Answer x = 10·4 m

Trigonometry: Solving problems

This diagram shows a man at the top of a cliff looking down at a boat.

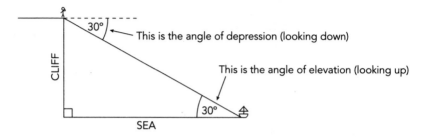

Note: The angle of depression from the top of the cliff is equal to the angle of elevation from the boat. (Remember Z angles from page 42.)

Angles of depression and angles of elevation are measured from the horizontal.

Answering questions

1   Read the question carefully.

2   It may help to visualise what is required. You can use objects such as pencils, rubbers, rulers to make a model of what is required.

3   Draw a diagram. Remember you need a right-angled triangle.

4   Read the question again. Check that your diagram is correct.

Question

Sarah is flying a kite. The string is 80 m long and the angle of elevation is 32°. How high is the kite?

Answer

Draw a diagram.

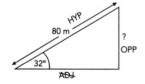  Cover up OPP

OPP = SIN x HYP
   = SIN32° x 80
   = 42·4 m

Locus

A couple of ruler and pair of compasses constructions. That's it. Very easy once you know how.

Locus (plural loci)

This is a mathematical name to describe the set of points which satisfy conditions. You will need to use a pair of compasses. Do NOT rub out your construction lines.

Questions

1   Draw the locus of a point which is always 0·75 cm from the line AB.

    A ——————————— B

2   Draw the locus of a point which is always an equal distance from two points P and Q which are 4 cm apart.

3   Draw the locus of a point which is always an equal distance from the lines BA and BC.

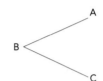

Answers

1   You must use a pair of compasses to draw the semi-circles at each end.

2   This is the locus of the point which is always an equal distance from P and Q

3   This is the locus of the point which is always an equal distance from BA and BC

Method

a   Open a pair of compasses. Keep them the same distance apart.
b   Place the pair of compasses on B.
c   Draw an arc on AB (1).
d   Draw an arc on BC (2).
e   Place the pair of compasses at 1 where the arc crosses the line AB.
f   Draw an arc (3).
g   Place the pair of compasses at 2 where the arc crosses the line BC.
h   Draw an arc (4).
i   Join B to the intersection of arcs 3 and 4.

Method

a   Join P and Q.
b   Place a pair of compasses on P.
c   Open the compasses over halfway towards Q.
d   Draw an arc above and below the line (1 and 2).
e   Keep the compasses the same distance apart.
f   Place the pair of compasses on Q.
g   Draw an arc above and below the line (3 and 4).
h   Join the intersections of both arcs. This is the locus.

Advice: Make sure you have a tight pair of compasses – drawing an arc is impossible if your compass slips.

Questionnaires

This may be useful for your coursework. It is quite easy. Just use your common sense.

Designing questionnaires

Questionnaires are used to obtain information. You may need to design a questionnaire as part of your coursework.

1 Design your questions to obtain information you can present and analyse in a variety of ways. A variety of different ways to present your data is given on pages 74-86.

2 Make your questions easy to understand.

3 Do not ask embarrassing questions, eg "How many boyfriends do you have?"

4 Provide a choice of answer, eg "Do you do a lot of homework?", will produce answers such as "yes", "sometimes", "only in Maths". These responses are difficult to present and analyse. A better question would be:

"How much time did you spend doing homework last night? Tick the box nearest to the amount of time."

0 hours ☐   1 hours ☐   2 hours ☐   3 hours ☐

Types of question

Your questionnaire should contain one or two questions of each of the following types:

1 Questions with yes/no responses, eg "Do you own a bicycle?" Yes ☐ No ☐

Try to avoid questions to which everyone will answer yes or everyone will answer no. Your results can be shown as a percentage, in a bar graph, pictogram, pie chart, etc.

2 Questions with numerical answers, eg "How many televisions do you have in your house?"

Your results can be presented in graphs, tables, etc. You can calculate the mean, median and mode of the data.

3 Questions you can compare, eg "What was your percentage mark in the English exam?" and "What was your percentage mark in the Maths exam?"

These questions will allow you to draw a scatter diagram to test a hypothesis such as "Pupils who obtain high marks in English also obtain high marks in Maths."

How many people to ask

Twenty is a good number. Each person represents 5% of the total and each person can be represented by 18° on a pie chart.

Forty is a good number. Each person represents 2.5% of the total and each person can be represented by 9° on a pie chart.

How many questions to ask

A maximum of ten.

Hypotheses

A hypothesis is an idea. Hypotheses can be tested in a variety of ways, eg observation, experiment, questionnaire.

Task

Choose a hypothesis. Decide how to test it. Collect data. Present the data in a variety of ways see pages 74-86. Analyse the data. Draw conclusions. Was the hypothesis correct?

What to do

1   Think of a hypothesis. A hypothesis is a statement or observation which may be true, eg "More men than women drive cars", "A drawing-pin lands point upwards more than point downwards", "Girls' favourite television channel is BBC1".

2   Decide how to test your hypothesis. How will you collect your data?
    The above hypotheses could be tested in these ways:

    • More men than women drive cars (observation).
    • A drawing-pin lands point upwards more than point downwards (experiment).
    • Girls' favourite television channel is BBC1 (questionnaire).

3   How will you analyse and present your data? The following should be included:

    • Tables – eg percentages
    • Graphs – pictograms, bar charts, line graphs
    • Pie charts – including your calculations
    • Frequency polygons
    • Averages – mean, median, mode
    • Range
    • Scatter diagrams – positive correlation, negative correlation, line of best fit
    • Cumulative frequency – upper quartile, lower quartile, inter-quartile range
    • Bias – are the results honest? For example, a coin could be weighted to give more heads than tails. If a teacher conducts a survey "How many hours of homework did you do last night?", some pupils might lie.

    If you can use a computer you could include spreadsheets, etc.

    Remember to make your graphs neat; try to use colour.

    Do not produce dozens of one type of graph. It is far better to draw three or four pie charts than 20 pie charts.

    Remember to state your hypothesis at the start.

    Remember to analyse your findings. Draw conclusions from your results. Justify your conclusions – is your hypothesis proved?

If your hypothesis does not allow you to analyse and present your data in a variety of ways it is far wiser to choose a different hypothesis **immediately**. Do not waste time on a hypothesis which will not allow you to demonstrate your mathematical ability.

Tables and graphs

Again much of this is common sense. You need to be able to read information from tables and graphs in everyday life.

Using and drawing conclusions from graphs

Information can be obtained from graphs. You need to know how to extract the information you need.

This is a conversion graph for changing miles into kilometres.

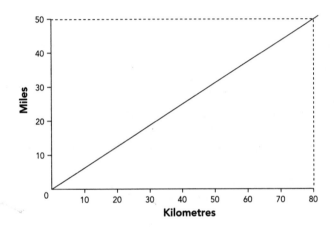

Examples

1   The distance from Exeter to Dorchester is 50 miles. How far is this in kilometres?

Method: Find 50 miles on the graph. Draw a dotted line from the 50 mile mark to the conversion line. Draw a dotted line from the point it meets the conversion line to the kilometres scale. The distance in 80 kilometres.

2   Convert 300 kilometres into miles.

Method: The scale does not have 300 kilometres. Use 30 kilometres instead. 30 is about 19 miles. Therefore 300 kilometres is about 190 miles.

Questions

1   Convert 50 kilometres into miles.

2   Convert 30 miles into kilometres.

Answers

1   31 or 32 miles   2   48 kilometres

Your answers need not be exact.

Frequency tables and frequency diagrams

Continuous data is data which can have any value, eg distance between two places, height of a person. The height of a person can be measured to any degree of accuracy. A person could be 1.783642 m tall.

Discrete data is data which can only have certain values, eg the number of people in a room can only have whole number values. You cannot have 3.2 people in a room.

If you are asked to collect data you must choose an appropriate method. Usually a survey or an experiment. You must record your data and then present it in tables, diagrams and graphs.

Questions

The following are the times taken by 20 people to complete a jigsaw. The times are in minutes:

8.62, 28.4, 48.13, 30.1, 26.03, 47.42, 36.01, 25.23, 22.6, 29.97, 18.63, 30.00, 42.73, 38.62, 20.01, 19.99, 27.6, 16.32, 8.7, 12.58

a   Record the information in a frequency table. Choose suitable equal class intervals.

b   Show this information in a frequency diagram.

Answers

a   A common error is:

Minutes
0 - 10
10 - 20
20 - 30

Where would you record 20?
In the 10-20 or 20-30?

Minutes	Tally	Frequency
0 - under 10	I I	2
10 - under 20	I I I I	4
20 - under 30	⊔⊔⊤ I I	7
30 - under 40	I I I I	4
40 - under 50	I I I	3

Advice: Always add the frequency total. ➞ 20
There are 20 people, therefore the
frequency must add up to 20.

b

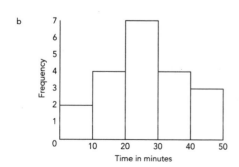

Time in minutes

Comparing data

Sometimes you will be asked to compare two sets of data. If you are comparing you must write about the similarities and differences of BOTH sets of data. A frequency polygon is a graph produced by joining up points with straight lines.

Questions

The heights of 20 boys and 20 girls aged 16 are shown in this table.

Height (cm)	Number of boys	Number of girls
140 – 149	–	1
150 – 159	1	3
160 – 169	6	8
170 – 179	8	6
180 – 189	4	2
190 – 199	1	–

1 Present the data in a frequency polygon.

2 Compare the distributions and comment on your findings.

Answers

1

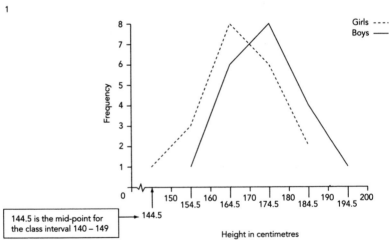

144.5 is the mid-point for the class interval 140 – 149 → 144.5

Height in centimetres

2 The frequency polygon shows that boys aged 16 are generally taller than girls of the same age.

Averages

There are three main types of average – mean, median and mode. You need to know each. Many students get them mixed up and that is just throwing away marks.

Median and mode

Median and mode are measures of average.

The **median** is the middle number when the numbers are placed in order.
The **mode** is the most common number.

Questions

1   Find the median and mode of these numbers:

2, 3, 5, 3, 2, 4, 2

2   Find the median of these numbers:

7, 3, 10, 2

3   The masses of boxers in a tournament are given in kilograms:

65, 63, 68, 64, 69, 68, 63, 64, 67, 69, 63, 61, 63, 67, 60

Find the median and the mode

Answers

1   First place the numbers in order of size

3 is the middle number, therefore the median is 3

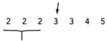

2   2   2   3   3   4   5

There are more 2s than any other number, therefore the mode is 2

2   Place the numbers in order

2   3   7   10

The median is between 3 and 7

$$\frac{3+7}{2} = \frac{10}{2} = 5$$

The median is 5

3   Place the numbers in order: 60, 61, 63, 63, 63, 63, 64, 64, 65, 67, 67, 68, 68, 69, 69

The median is 64

The mode is 63

Mean and range

The **mean** is the most useful average because it uses all of the data. The mean is sometimes called the arithmetic mean.

The **range** is the difference between the largest and smallest numbers.

Example

a   Find the mean of: 16, 18, 11, 19, 17   b   Find the range

Method

a   Add the numbers, then divide by how many numbers there are.

$$\frac{16 + 18 + 11 + 19 + 17}{5} = \frac{81}{5} = 16 \cdot 2$$

b   The range is $19 - 11 = 8$

Questions

1   There are four children in a room. Their ages are: 16, 14, 13 and 15.

   a   What is the mean of their ages?

   b   What is the range?

2   This table show the number of letters delivered to houses in a street:

Letters	0	1	2	3	4	5
Number of houses	3	2	6	7	0	2

   Calulate the mean number of letters delivered to each house.

3   The mean of four numbers is 7. The numbers are 5, 3, 8 and x. Find x.

Answers

1   a $\frac{16 + 14 + 13 + 15}{4} = \frac{58}{4} = 14 \cdot 5$

   b $16 - 13 = 3$

2   This is a very common exam question (question 3, page 80 *Grouped data* is very similar).

> Two **common errors** are $\frac{0+1+2+3+4+5}{6} = 2 \cdot 5$ and $\frac{0+1+2+3+4+5}{3+2+6+7+0+2} = \frac{15}{20} = 0 \cdot 75$

$\text{mean} = \frac{\text{total number of letters}}{\text{total number of houses}} = \frac{(0 \times 3) + (1 \times 2) + (2 \times 6) + (3 \times 7) + (4 \times 0) + (5 \times 2)}{3 + 2 + 6 + 7 + 0 + 2} = \frac{45}{20} = 2 \cdot 25$

3   The mean of four numbers is 7. Therefore, the total is $4 \times 7 = 28$.

     $5 + 3 + 8 + x = 28$

         $16 + x = 28$

            $x = 12$

Comparing two sets of data

The mean, median or mode can be used as a measure of average.

If a question asks you to compare two lists of information, you must write about the differences between the lists.

If you have a choice, it is easiest to compare by using the mean. It is most difficult to compare by using the mode.

Question

These are the Maths test results (out of ten marks) for Jenny and Paul:

Test	1	2	3	4	5	6	7	8	9	10
Jenny's marks	8	6	8	5	4	6	7	6	8	4
Paul's marks	9	10	9	8	3	4	1	8	9	10

Use the range and mean to compare their marks. Who is better at Maths and why?

Answer

Jenny's range of marks is 8 – 4 = 4

Paul's range of marks is 10 – 1 = 9

> You should compare the ranges

Jenny's marks have a smaller range. This suggests that she is more consistent than Paul. Jenny always gains a satisfactory mark. Paul scores some very good marks and some very poor marks.

Jenny's mean mark is $\frac{62}{10}$ = 6·2

Paul's mean mark is $\frac{71}{10}$ = 7·1

The mean marks suggest Paul is slightly better at Maths but the range suggests that he is very good in some areas and very poor in other areas.

If a test question asks you who is better, you can state either person but you must give a reason based on the range and mean, median or mode.

Grouped data

Information is often grouped. We can estimate the median, mean and range.

Questions

This table shows the number of cars using a car park over a period of 100 days:

Number of cars	0 – 99	100 – 199	200 – 299	300 – 399	400 – 500
Frequency	5	18	30	27	20

1 What is the modal class?
2 Estimate the median
3 Estimate the mean

Answers

1 The modal class is the class with the highest number. In this question it is 200 – 299 cars.

2 There are 100 days. The median is the middle day when arranged in order of size. The question asks for an estimate, therefore we can assume that the median is the 50th day.

  5 + 18 = 23. Therefore there are 23 days with less than 200 cars.

  5 + 18 + 30 = 53. Therefore there are 53 days with less than 300 cars.

  The 50th day is towards the high end of the 200 – 299 class.

  A good estimate of the median would be about 290 cars.

3 This question is similar to question 2 on page 78 *Mean and range*.

  The mean is found by first multiplying the mid–value of each class by the frequency. The question asks for an estimate, therefore we can use 50, 150, 250, 350 and 450 as the mid–values.

  $$\frac{(5 \times 50) + (18 \times 150) + (30 \times 250) + (27 \times 350) + (20 \times 450)}{100}$$

  $$= \frac{250 + 2700 + 7500 + 9450 + 9000}{100}$$

  $$= \frac{28900}{100}$$

  The mean number of cars is about 289.

Cumulative frequency

Cumulative frequency is very likely to appear on your exam paper. Just learn the rules.

Cumulative frequency

We can use cumulative frequency curves to compare data.

Questions

This table shows the marks of pupils in an exam:

Mark	Frequency
6-15	3
16-25	10
26-35	14
36-45	28
46-55	20
56-65	5

1 What is the range of the marks?

2 Draw a cumulative frequency diagram

3 What is the median mark?

4 What is the upper quartile?

5 What is the lower quartile?

6 What is the interquartile range?

7 Pupils need 50 or over for an 'A' grade. How many 'A' grades were awarded?

Answers

1 The range is 65 – 6 = 59

2 First complete a cumulative frequency column

Mark	Frequency	Cumulative Frequency
6-15	3	3
16-25	10	3+10 = 13
26-35	14	3+10+14 = 27
36-45	28	3+10+14+28 = 55
46-55	20	3+10+14+28+20 = 75
56-65	5	3+10+14+28+20+5 = 80

Note: Points are plotted at the maximum value of the class interval, eg the 46–55 interval is plotted at (55,75) not (50,75).

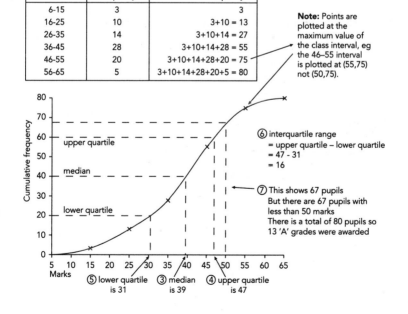

⑥ interquartile range
= upper quartile – lower quartile
= 47 - 31
= 16

⑦ This shows 67 pupils
But there are 67 pupils with less than 50 marks
There is a total of 80 pupils so 13 'A' grades were awarded

⑤ lower quartile is 31   ③ median is 39   ④ upper quartile is 47

Using cumulative frequency diagrams to compare distributions

Question

Two different makes of light bulbs were compared. The cumulative frequency diagrams show the number of hours the bulbs lasted.

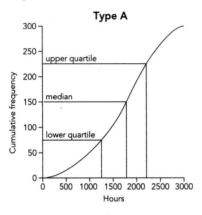

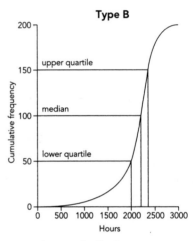

Use the median and interquartile range to compare the two distributions.

Answer

Different numbers of bulbs were used in the tests but the median and interquartile range allow comparison between the two types of bulb. The interquartile range measures the range of the middle half of the distribution.

The median of bulb A is about 1800 hours.
The median of bulb B is about 2200 hours.
This implies that bulb B is better because the median bulb lasts 400 hours longer.

The interquartile range of bulb A is about (2200 – 1250) 950 hours.
The interquartile range of bulb B is about (2400 – 2000) 400 hours.

The middle half of bulb B is bunched together, ie steeper curve.
The middle half of bulb A is more spread out.

The information suggests that bulbs of type B are more consistent and have a longer lifetime.

Scatter diagrams

These are used to find connections between two sets of data.

Scatter diagrams

Scatter diagrams are used to find relationships (or correlation) between two sets of data.

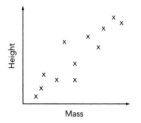

Mass

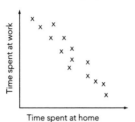

Time spent at home

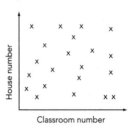

Classroom number

This diagram shows a
positive correlation

This diagram shows a
negative correlation

This diagram shows
no correlation

A positive correlation indicates that as one quantity increases so does the other quantity. The diagram shows that, in general, taller people are heavier.

A negative correlation indicates that as one quantity increases the other quantity decreases. The diagram shows that, in general, the more time a person spends at work, the less time they spend at home.

No correlation indicates that there is no relationship between the two quantities. The diagram shows that a house number has no connection with the classroom number.

> **Note:** Remember to use the word correlation in your answer.

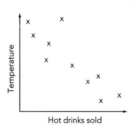

Hot drinks sold

Questions

1   Describe the relationship shown by this scatter diagram.

2   Explain the reason for this relationship.

Answers

1   Negative correlation.

   As the temperature increases, the number of hot drinks sold decreases.

   or As the temperature decreases, the number of hot drinks sold increases.

2   In hot weather people drink fewer hot drinks.

   In cold weather people drink more hot drinks.

Line of best fit

A line of best fit is drawn by looking at the crosses on a scatter diagram and then drawing a line. Normally there would be a similar number of crosses above the line as below the line.

Questions

1   Draw a line of best fit on this scatter diagram. This scatter diagram shows the masses of 16 pupils against their ages.

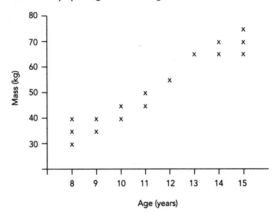

2   Use your line of best fit to estimate the mass of a 13 year old pupil.

Answers

1   The line of best fit should be in a similar position to the line shown.

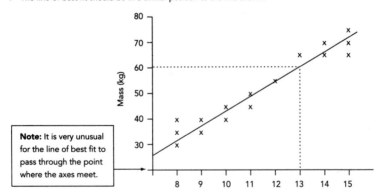

Note: It is very unusual for the line of best fit to pass through the point where the axes meet.

2   **Method:** Draw a line from 13 years to the line of best fit. Read the mass.

The answer should be about 60 kg.

Pie charts

Look back at the angles section (see page 40). Pie charts allow us to present information. Information presented in a diagram is often easier to understand than information in a table.

Understanding pie charts

You will be expected to read information from pie charts and draw pie charts.

Questions

This pie chart shows how the pupils in class 3A arrive at school:

1   How many pupils walk to school?

2   What is the angle for the bus sector?

3   How many pupils attend the school?

4   Complete the car sector

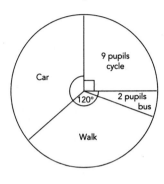

Answers

The first thing to do is find the angle for one pupil.

The pie chart shows 9 pupils cycle to school. This sector is 90°.

9 pupils are represented by 90°

1 pupil is represented by 10°

1   The angle for the walk sector is 120°
    We know that 1 pupil is represented by 10°
    Therefore **12 pupils** are represented by 120°
2   2 pupils arrive by bus
    We know that 1 pupil is represented by 10°
    Therefore 2 pupils are represented by **20°**
3   There are 360° in a circle
    We know that 1 pupil is represented by 10°
    Therefore **36 pupils** are represented by 360°
4   The angles of a circle add up to 360°
    cycle + bus + walk + car = 360°
    90° + 20° + 120° + x = 360°
    The angle for the car sector is **130°**
    The pupils add up to 36
    cycle + bus + walk + car = 36
    9 + 2 + 12 + y = 36
    13 pupils arrive by car

Drawing pie charts

Question

Thirty people were asked what sort of holiday they would choose. 5 said a mountain resort, 10 said a beach holiday, 7 said an activity holiday and 8 said a cruise. Show this information in a pie chart.

Answer

The first thing to do is find the angle for one person. There are 360° in a circle. The pie chart must represent 30 people.

$360° \div 30 = 12°$ Therefore 12° represents 1 person.

Holiday choice	Frequency	Multiply by 12°	Angle at the centre of the pie chart
Mountain resort	5	x 12°	60°
Beach holiday	10	x 12°	120°
Activity holiday	7	x 12°	84°
Cruise	8	x 12°	96°

How to draw the pie chart

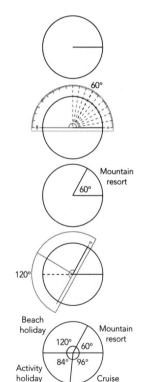

1 Draw a circle.

   Draw a line from the centre to the edge.

2 Place the protractor on the circle.

   Place the centre of the protractor on the centre of the circle.

   Make sure 0° is on the line.

   Measure the first angle, 60°.

3 Draw a line from the centre to the edge at 60°.

   Label the sector "Mountain resort" and write 60°.

4 Move the protractor as shown.

   Measure 120°.

   Draw a line from the centre to the edge.

5 Repeat for 84°.

   Check the remaining angle is 96°.

   Label each sector.

Do not forget: Label each sector and show the angle size.

Measure the angles carefully. If angles are not accurate, you will lose marks.

Probability

You need to understand when to multiply probabilities, when to add probabilities and tree diagrams.

The probability scale

The probability scale is used to show the chance of something happening. If something is impossible, eg picking a red disk from a bag of white disks, we say there is no chance and the probability is 0. If something will definitely happen, eg picking a white disk from a bag of white disks, we say it is certain and the probability is 1.

This is a probability scale:

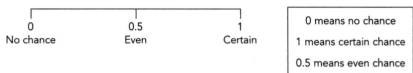

0	0.5	1
No chance	Even	Certain

> 0 means no chance
>
> 1 means certain chance
>
> 0.5 means even chance

Questions

David, Paul and Adam are each blindfolded. Each chooses a ball from one of three bags. Their chances of choosing a black ball are shown on the probability scale.

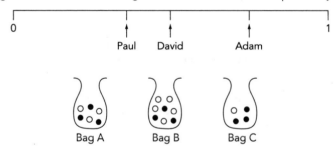

Bag A   Bag B   Bag C

Who chooses from:

1   Bag A
2   Bag B
3   Bag C?

Answers

1   3 out of 6 is an even chance. David chooses from Bag A.
2   3 out of 8 is less than an even chance. Paul chooses from Bag B.
3   3 out of 4 is more than an even chance. Adam chooses from Bag C.

Justifying probabilities

You can decide the probability of something happening by:

equally likely outcomes or experimental evidence.

We use equally likely outcomes for events with equal chances.

Eg: Throwing a die

The chance of throwing each number is equal. There are six numbers. The chance of throwing each number is $1/_6$.

Sometimes events do not have equal chances. Then we must use experimental evidence.

Eg: The chances of a bus being late or on time are not equal.
We must observe and record the bus for a period of time.

Questions

1   Alan and Barry are in a race. Is it true that each boy has an equal chance of winning? If not, why not?

2   A coin is tossed. What is the chance of it landing on a head and why?

3   Toss a coin 20 times. Repeat the experiment five times. Do we always get the same number of heads and tails? Explain your answer.

Answers

1   It is very unlikely that each boy has an equal chance of winning. One of the boys is probably a better runner. The best way to decide the chances would be to observe the boys in, for example, ten races, ie experimental evidence. You would then know who was better.

2   There is an equal chance of a head or a tail, ie equally likely outcomes. The chance of a head is $1/_2$.

3   We would expect an equal number of heads and tails each time. But this will not happen every time. Probability is a theoretical expectation. It is not a guarantee.

Estimation of probability by experiment

We can carry out an experiment to help us to estimate probability, eg we could throw a thousand drawing-pins and count how many times they landed point up. This would allow us to use the probability to estimate how many would land point up if a million drawing-pins were thrown.

The more times an experiment is carried out, the more likely the data obtained is accurate.

Example

A six-sided die is thrown. Here are the results:

Side of die	1	2	3	4	5	6
John	2	7	3	8	4	6
Andrea	46	51	53	47	46	57

John threw the die 30 times.
Andrea threw the die 300 times.

Andrea is more likely to obtain the better estimate because she has thrown the die more times than John.

Questions

A die is thrown 600 times. These results are obtained.

1	2	3	4	5	6
102	112	181	31	82	92

1   Do the results indicate the die is biased?

2   Justify your answer.

3   Use the data to work out the probability of the die landing on:

   a 1, b 3, c 4, d 6

4   If the die were fair how many times would you expect it to land on each number if it were thrown 600 times?

Answers

1   The die seems to be biased.

2   More 3s were obtained than would be expected by chance. Fewer 4s were obtained than would be expected by chance.

3   a $^{102}/_{600} = ^{51}/_{300} = ^{17}/_{100}$ b $^{181}/_{600}$

   c $^{31}/_{600}$ d $^{92}/_{600} = ^{23}/_{150}$

4   We would expect the die to land on each number a similar amount of times. The chance of each number is $^{1}/_{6}$. Therefore we would expect each number to occur about 100 times.

Probability: Examination-type questions

Here are some examples of the questions you can expect to find on examination papers.

Questions

1 Draw a tree diagram to show all of the possible outcomes when two coins are tossed.

2 a Complete this table to show all of the possible outcomes when throwing two dice.

	1	2	3	4	5	6
1						
2						
3						
4						
5						
6						

   b How many different ways can two dice land?

   c What is the probability of a double?

3 The probability of a new light bulb not working is 0.03. What is the probability of a new light bulb working?

Answers

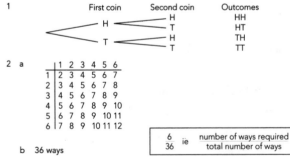

1

First coin	Second coin	Outcomes
H	H	HH
	T	HT
T	H	TH
	T	TT

2 a

	1	2	3	4	5	6
1	2	3	4	5	6	7
2	3	4	5	6	7	8
3	4	5	6	7	8	9
4	5	6	7	8	9	10
5	6	7	8	9	10	11
6	7	8	9	10	11	12

$\dfrac{6}{36}$ ie $\dfrac{\text{number of ways required}}{\text{total number of ways}}$

   b 36 ways

   c There are 6 doubles

   There are 36 different ways

   Probability = $^{6}/_{36}$ = $^{1}/_{6}$

3 A light bulb can either work or not work so the total probability is 1.

Probability of working	+	probability of not working	=	1
?	+	0·03	=	1
Probability of working			=	1 – 0·03
Probability of working			=	0·97

Probability (and, or)

This page shows ways to calculate probablility.

A bag contains three red sweets, four blue sweets and five white sweets. A boy is blindfolded. He chooses a sweet. What is the probability he chooses:

a   A red sweet

b   A blue sweet

c   A red sweet or a blue sweet?

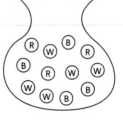

Method

a $\dfrac{3}{12}$ ◄— There are three red sweets in the bag
       ◄— There are twelve sweets in the bag

b $\dfrac{4}{12}$ ◄— There are four blue sweets in the bag
       ◄— There are twelve sweets in the bag

c   If a question states 'or' we must add

      Probablilty of a red sweet   or   Probability of a blue sweet

            $\dfrac{3}{12}$ + $\dfrac{4}{12}$

(use the fraction key to add the fractions)

$$\boxed{3}\ \boxed{a^{b}_{c}}\ \boxed{1}\ \boxed{2}\ \boxed{+}\ \boxed{4}\ \boxed{a^{b}_{c}}\ \boxed{1}\ \boxed{2}\ \boxed{=}$$

Answer $^{7}/_{12}$

Questions

1   What is the probability of choosing a white sweet?

2   What is the probability of choosing a red sweet or a white sweet?

Answers

1   $^{5}/_{12}$ ◄— There are five white sweets in the bag
       ◄— There are twelve sweets in the bag

2   Probability of a red sweet   or   Probability of a white sweet

           $^{3}/_{12}$ + $^{5}/_{12}$

Calculator keys:
Answer $^{2}/_{3}$ $\boxed{3}\ \boxed{a^{b}_{c}}\ \boxed{1}\ \boxed{2}\ \boxed{+}\ \boxed{5}\ \boxed{a^{b}_{c}}\ \boxed{1}\ \boxed{2}\ \boxed{=}$

Probability (at least)

This page shows you a shortcut. This is used when a question asks for the probability of "at least" or the "probability of not getting".

Questions

Three coins are tossed.

What is the probability of:

1   Exactly one head?

2   At least one head?

Answers

1   We need:

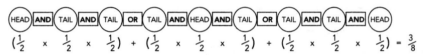

$$(\tfrac{1}{2} \times \tfrac{1}{2} \times \tfrac{1}{2}) + (\tfrac{1}{2} \times \tfrac{1}{2} \times \tfrac{1}{2}) + (\tfrac{1}{2} \times \tfrac{1}{2} \times \tfrac{1}{2}) = \tfrac{3}{8}$$

(Or you could use a tree diagram, see page 93.)

2   Remember, the total probability for all of the possible ways three coins can land is 1. We could say:

(HEAD) **AND** (HEAD) **AND** (HEAD) **OR** (HEAD) **AND** (HEAD) **AND** (TAIL) **OR** . . .

This will work but it takes a long time!

Think carefully

Sometimes it is quicker to work out the probability of what we do not want.

What don't we want?

We don't want three tails. Any other outcome will contain at least one head.

The probability of three tails is:

(TAIL) **AND** (TAIL) **AND** (TAIL)

$$\tfrac{1}{2} \times \tfrac{1}{2} \times \tfrac{1}{2} = \tfrac{1}{8}$$

Total probability – Probability of three tails = Probability of at least one head

$$1 \quad - \quad \tfrac{1}{8} \quad = \quad \tfrac{7}{8}$$

> **Note:** When a question states "at least" always consider the short cut
>
> Total probability – what we do not want = what we do want

Tree diagrams

Tree diagrams can be used to work out the probability of events.

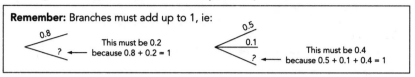

Remember: Branches must add up to 1, ie:

0.8

This must be 0.2
? ← because 0.8 + 0.2 = 1

0.5
0.1

This must be 0.4
? ← because 0.5 + 0.1 + 0.4 = 1

Questions

A car driver passes through two sets of traffic lights on his way to work. The lights can either be red or green. The probability of red at the first lights is 0.6. The probability of red at the second lights is 0.3.

Draw a tree diagram to show this and hence calculate the probability that:

1   Both lights are red

2   Both lights are green

3   One set of lights is red and one is green

4   At least one set of lights is red

Answers

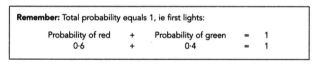

Remember: Total probability equals 1, ie first lights:

| Probability of red | + | Probability of green | = | 1 |
| 0·6 | + | 0·4 | = | 1 |

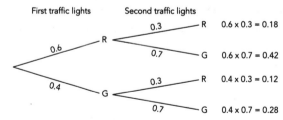

First traffic lights   Second traffic lights

0.6
R
0.3 — R   0.6 x 0.3 = 0.18
0.7 — G   0.6 x 0.7 = 0.42

0.4
G
0.3 — R   0.4 x 0.3 = 0.12
0.7 — G   0.4 x 0.7 = 0.28

1   0.18

2   0.28

3   Red and green or green and red   0.42 + 0.12 = 0.54

4   Red and red or red and green or green and red   0.18 + 0.42 + 0.12 = 0.72

Alternative method

The question states "at least". Look at the previous page *Probability (at least)*.

Total probability	–	what we do not want	=	what we do want
1	–	green and green	=	what we do want
1	–	0.28	=	0.72

Sample exam questions

1   Here are some patterns made with matchsticks:

   a Draw the next triangle pattern in this sequence.

   b Complete this table:

Number of triangles	1	2	3	4	5	6
Number of matchsticks	3	5				

   c Complete this formula:

     M =   T   T represents triangles
                          M represents matchsticks

  d   Use your formula to find:

     i   How many matchsticks are needed to make 50 triangles?

     ii How many triangles can be formed with 275 matchsticks?

2   a Mr Jones earned £240 per week. He received a 6% pay rise.
      What was his new salary?

    b Mrs Jones earned £15 000 per year. She received a pay increase of £1200.
      What percentage pay rise did she receive?

3   Complete this phone bill:

	£	
Standing charge	20	
300 units at 4p each		(a)
Total		(b)
Plus 17.5% VAT		(c)
Total payable		(d)

4   A ladder is placed against a wall.

The ladder is 3.5 m long.

The angle between the ladder and the ground is 67°.

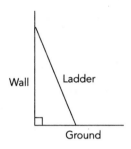

a   What is the distance from the top of the ladder to the ground?

b   What is the distance from the bottom of the ladder to the wall?

c   The ladder is moved so that the top of the ladder is 3.35 m above the ground.
    Calculate the angle between the ladder and the wall.

5   A classroom is measured. It is 780 cm correct to the nearest centimetre.

a   What is the maximum length of the classroom?

b   What is the minimum length of the classroom?

Answers

1 a

    b

Number of triangles	1	2	3	4	5	6
Number of matchsticks	3	5	7	9	11	13

    c   M = 2T + 1   [see page 18]

    d   i   M = 2 x 50 + 1

            M = 101   [see page 18]

        ii   275 = 2T +1

          275 – 1 = 2T

            274 = 2T

            $\frac{274}{2}$ = T

            137 = T   [see question 5 page 23]

2 a   240 x £1.06 = £254.40   [see page 17]

      Common error: The calculator shows £254.4 but this will lose marks. The correct answer is £254.40.

    b   1200 ÷ 15 000 x 100 = **8%**

      or using a calculator   ⬚1⬚ ⬚2⬚ ⬚0⬚ ⬚0⬚ ⬚÷⬚ ⬚1⬚ ⬚5⬚ ⬚0⬚ ⬚0⬚ ⬚0⬚ ⬚%⬚   [see page 16]

3 a   300 x 4p = £12

      A **common error** is to write £1200

    b   £20 + £12 = **£32**

    c   £32 x 0.175 = **£5.60**

    d   £32 + £5.60 = **£37.60**   [see page 17]

4 a

$\sin = \dfrac{\text{opp}}{\text{hyp}}$

opp = sin x hyp

Answer 3·22 m   [see page 69]

    b

Use Pythagoras' theorem   [see page 67]

$$y^2 = 3\!\cdot\!5^2 - 3\!\cdot\!221766987^2$$

Note: You must use **all** of the numbers in your calculator, ie 3·221766987. Do **not** shorten to 3·22

Answer 1·36755895 m (1·37 m correct to 3 significant figures)

    c

$\cos = \dfrac{\text{adj}}{\text{hyp}}$ [see page 68]

Answer 16·83498067° (16·8° correct to 3 significant figures)

5 a   780.5 cm

    b   779.5 cm

Diagnostic tests

These tests will help you check how good you are at questions on each topic. If you have difficulty, revise the topic again.

1 Negative numbers
1 Place these numbers in order, smallest first: −1, 0, 3, −5, 2
2 −8 + 3 =
3 −5 − 2 =

2 Mental arithmetic shortcuts − 1
1 600 × 80 =
2 5600 ÷ 70 =

3 Mental arithmetic shortcuts − 2
1 42·3 × 100 =
2 3·82 ÷ 1000 =

4 Decimals
1 3·6 + 42 + 0·38 =
2 8·3 − 2·71 =
3 5·62 × 0·03 =
4 4·2 ÷ 0·06 =

5 Long multiplication and division
1 523 × 74
2 665 ÷ 17

6 Checking − 1
1 Write out a subtraction sum to check this sum:

```
  7 3 2
+ 1 8 9
  9 2 1
```

2 Estimate the cost of 407 tapes at £3.95 each.

7 Checking − 2
1 Estimate 812 ÷ 0·019
2 600 × 0·04
3 40 ÷ 0·002

8 Using a calculator: Brackets and memory
1 6·41(3·72 − 8·532)
2 $\dfrac{6.87 - (9.36 \times 3.4)}{8.42 \times 0.164}$

9 Using a calculator: Powers, roots, memory
1 A cube has a volume of 216 cm³. What is the length of each side?
2 What is the value of 5^4?
3 Calculate the value of:
   a $2401^{3/4}$ b $\sqrt[5]{243}$

10 Standard form
1 Write 6.32×10^{-4} as an ordinary number.
2 Write 273 000 in standard form.
3 Write 0·0072 in standard form.
4 $8.42 \times 10^{-6} \div 3.4 \times 10^{-2}$

11 Fractions
1 Find $^5/_{16}$ of 4
2 72 people out of 88 watched *Neighbours*. Write this as a fraction in its lowest terms.
3 $5^3/_4 \div 1^2/_3$

12 Changing between decimals and percentages
1 Write 27·3% as a decimal.
2 Write 0·038 as a percentage.

13 Changing between decimals, percentages and fractions
1 Convert 0·024 to a fraction.
2 Write $^3/_8$ as a decimal.
3 Write $^4/_5$ as a percentage.

14 Ratio – 1

1 Simplify the ratio 36:27

2 The scale of a map is 1:50 000. The distance from Hilton to Longden is 12 cm on the map. What is the actual distance? Give your answer in kilometres.

15 Ratio – 2

1 A sum of money was divided between Alan and Barry in the ratio 3:5. Alan received £150.

   a How much did Barry receive?

   b What was the total amount of money?

16 Percentages

1 14 people out of 80 wore a hat. Write this as a percentage.

2 A man bought a painting for £500. Two years later he sold it for £650. Calculate the percentage gain.

3 A woman bought a vase for £60. She sold it for £48. Calculate the percentage loss.

17 Percentages and fractions

1 A cinema holds 3200 people. Safety regulations require the capacity to be reduced by $^3/_8$. What is the capacity after the reduction?

2 Mrs Saunders earned £240 per week. She received a 6% increase. What was her wage after the increase?

3 Mr Williams earned £180 per week in 1990. He received a 4% rise each year for five years. Calculate his wage in 1995.

4 Miss Soames bought a car for £10 000. The car depreciated by 10% each year. How much was it worth after four years?

18 Exploring number patterns

a What are the next two numbers in this pattern?

   4, 7, 10, 13, 16...

b What is the rule to produce this pattern?

c What is 120th term?

19 Patterns you must recognise

1 What are the special names given to these number patterns?

   a 1, 4, 9, 16, 25, 36...

   b 1, 8, 27, 64, 125, 216...

   c 1, 3, 6, 10, 15, 21...

2 List the factors of 30.

3 Complete the next three prime numbers:

   2, 3, 5, 7...

20 Product of primes, highest common factor, lowest common multiple and reciprocals

1 Write 1960 as a product of primes.

2 Find the HCF and LCM of 36 and 90.

3 Find the reciprocal of –8

21 Writing in algebra

1 A cake costs y pence. What is the cost of seven cakes?

2 S sweets are divided equally between four children. How many sweets does each child receive?

22 Using algebra

1 Find the value of the following formulae, when $x = 6$, $y = 4$, $z = 2$

a $3x$

b $2y - z$

c $3xy$

2 $T = AB + 4C$. Calculate T when $A = 4$, $B = 3$ and $C = 2$

23 Rules

Solve these equations:

1 $y + 7 = 10$

2 $y - 3 = -8$

3 $6y = 27$

4 $y/_4 = 3$

24 Writing equations

A man buys x books at £7 each. The total cost is £63.

1 Form an equation to show this

2 Solve the equation

25 Trial and improvement

1 Find the value of x correct to one decimal place using trial and improvement. You must show all of your working.

$x^2 + x = 27$

26 Harder equations

Solve these equations. Give the answer correct to three significant figures where appropriate.

1 $y^2 = 10$

2 $\sqrt{y} = 17$

3 $5/y = 8$

4 $3(y + 6) - 2(4y - 1) = 8$

27 Rewriting formulae

Make y the subject:

1 $\sqrt{y} = 4c$

2 $y^2 = 25x^2$

3 $A/_y = B$

28 Using algebraic formulae

$a = 1/_5$, $b = 2.3$, $c = -3.7$, $d = -4/_5$

Find the value of:

1 $6(4a - 3d)$

2 $\sqrt{\left(\dfrac{a^2 + b^2}{-3c}\right)}$

3 $\left(\dfrac{3a^2 + b^2}{c^2 - d}\right)$

4 $v = \pi r^2 h$

a Calculate v when $r = 3$, $h = 4$

b Calculate h when $r = 10$, $v = 400$

c Calculate r when $h = 5$, $v = 300$

29 Expansion of brackets

Simplify:

1 $a^5 \times a^3$

2 $4a^4 \times 3a$

3 $8a^6 \div 2a^{-4}$

Expand:

4 $5a(4a^2 x - 3ac)$

5 $2a^2 c^3 (3ad^2 + 4a^2 c)$

6 $(2a - 4)(3a - 5)$

30-32 Factorisation

Factorise:

1 $12a^2 - 4ac$

2 $15a^2 c^2 d + 25a^3 c$

3 $a^2 - 7a + 10$

4 Solve $a^2 - 7a + 10 = 0$

33 Simultaneous equations: Solving using algebra

Solve the simultaneous equations

$3a - 2y = 16$ $5a - 3y = 26$

34 Drawing lines

Draw and label the following lines

1 $y = 0$ 2 $x = 0$
3 $y = 4$ 4 $x = -3$
5 $y = x$ 6 $y = -x$

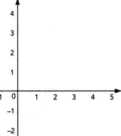

35 Simultaneous equations: Solving by drawing a graph

1 Solve the pair of simultaneous equations by drawing a graph.

$2y - x = 6$ $y + 2x = 8$

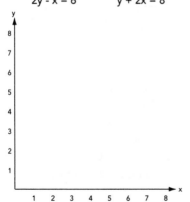

36 The straight line equation $y = mx + c$

What is the equation of the line which passes through the points (2,0) and (6,6)?

37 Drawing graphs

Label the following graphs.

Choose from:

$y = 2x^2 + 2$
$y = -3x^2 + 2$
$y = 2x + 2$
$y = -2x + 2$
$y = 1/x$
$y = -1/x$
$y = x^3$
$y = -x^3$

38 Speed, time and distance graphs

This graph shows the journey made by a car from Poole to Basingstoke:

1 What time did the car arrive in Basingstoke?

2 What was the speed of the car on the first part of its journey?

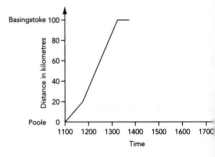

3 The car stayed in Basingstoke for
half an hour and then returned to
Poole at the speed of 40 km/h.

a Complete the graph

b What time did the car arrive
back in Poole?

39 Inequalities

Solve these inequalities:

1 $6x < 24$

2 $x - 3 > -5$

3 $-3x \leq -12$

4 $14 \leq 3x - 1 < 23$

5 Describe the shaded region.

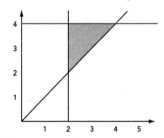

40 Using a protractor

Use a protractor to measure these
angles.

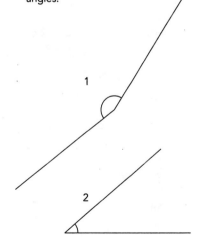

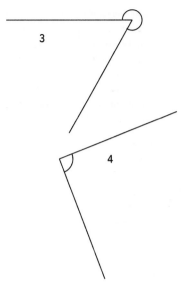

41 Angles: Acute, obtuse, reflex

Look at the angles for question 40
again. Name them. Choose from:

acute angle

obtuse angle

right angle

reflex angle.

42 Intersecting and parallel lines

Look at the diagram below.

1 Find the size of the missing angles.

2 Angle c and angle e are

3 Angle a and angle d are

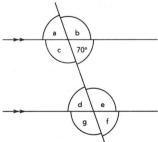

43 Regular polygons

1 Find the size of each exterior angle of a regular pentagon.

2 Find the size of each interior angle of a regular pentagon.

3 A regular polygon has an exterior angle of 18°. How many sides does it have?

44 Bearings

In the diagram below, A, B and C are three ships.

1 What is the bearing of A from B?

2 What is the bearing of B from A?

3 What is the bearing of B from C?

A ·

N

· B

·
C

45 2-D representation of 3-D shapes

1 Name the 3-D shape formed by this net:

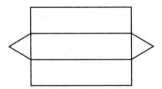

2 This net will form a cube:

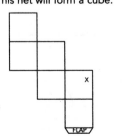

a Place an x in each corner which touches x when the cube is formed.

b Mark F on the edge to show where the flap will fit when the cube is formed.

46, 47 Properties of quadrilaterals and triangles

Name these shapes:

1

2

3

4 Complete this diagram to make a kite.

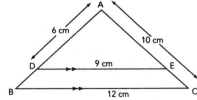

48 Similarity

AC = 8 cm   BC = 12 cm
AD = 6 cm   DE = 9 cm

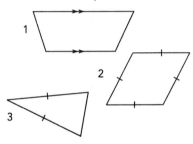

Find the length of:

1 AE

2 AB

3 BD

49 Rotational symmetry

Look at these shapes. If a shape does not have rotational symmetry write "no rotational symmetry". If it does have rotational symmetry, write the order and mark the centre of rotation with an x.

1

2

3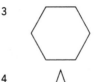

4

Reflection

Reflect these shapes in the mirror lines

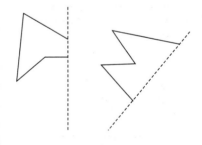

50, 51 Symmetry of 2-D shapes – 1

Draw the axes of symmetry of these shapes.

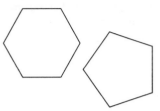

Draw the axes of symmetry on these shapes.

1

2 -

3

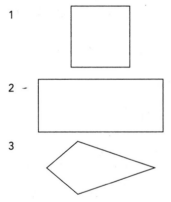

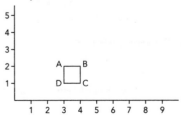

52, 53 Enlargement

Enlarge the square ABCD by a scale factor of 3. Centre of enlargement is the point (2,1).

54 Enlargement by a fractional scale factor

Enlarge the triangle A by a scale factor of $^1/_2$. Centre of enlargement is the point (7,3).

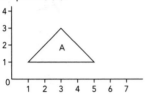

55 Translations

1 Which vector translates A to B?

2 Translate B by the vector $\begin{pmatrix} -3 \\ 2 \end{pmatrix}$. Label this C.

3 Which vector translates C to A?

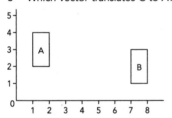

56 Rough metric equivalents of Imperial units

1 My garden is 20 yards long. How many metres is this approximately?

2 I bought ten pounds of potatoes. How many kilograms is this approximately?

57 Converting one metric unit to another

1 Convert 0.36 kilometres into metres.

2 Convert 850 millilitres into litres.

58 Making sensible estimates

This man is standing by a tree. Estimate the height of the tree.

59 Accuracy of measurement

The length of a room was measured as 7.32 m correct to the nearest centimetre.

1 What is the maximum length of the room?

2 What is the minimum length of the room?

60 Compound measures

1 A car travels 324 kilometres in 3 hours 52 minutes. Calculate the speed in kilometres per hour.

2 A car travels at 25 metres per second. What is this speed in kilometres per hour?

61 Time

1 A ferry leaves Poole at 21:47 on Wednesday and arrives in Cherbourg at 06:18 on Thursday. How long did the journey take?

2 A car travels 321 kilometres at an average speed of 57 km/h. How long does the journey take? Give your answer to:

a the nearest minute

b the nearest second.

62 Formulae

1. This is a semicircle.
   What is the size of angle x?

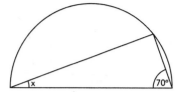

2. Find the:
   a circumference and
   b area of a circle, diameter 30 cm.

3. The area of a circle is 70 m². Calculate the radius.

4. Calculate the volume of a cylinder radius 4 cm, height 7 cm.

5. Find the:
   a area and
   b circumference of this shape.

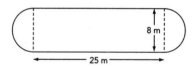

6. The diameter of this circular pond is 10 m. A path, 3 m wide, goes all the way around. Find the area of the path.

63 Calculating length, area and volume – 1

1. Calculate the area:

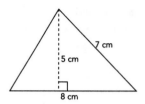

2. Calculate the area:

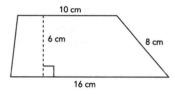

3. The volume of a cuboid is 144 cm³. The length is 8 cm, the width is 6 cm. Calculate the height.

64 Calculating length, area and volume – 2

Find the volume of these shapes.

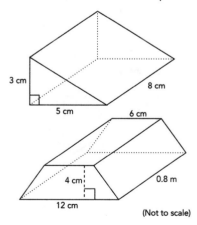

(Not to scale)

65 Calculating length, area and volume – 3

Find:

1 the area and

2 the perimeter of this shape.

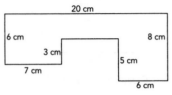

66 Formulae for length, area and volume

a, b, c and d are lengths. State whether each formula gives a length, area, volume or none of these:

1 $4\pi r$ 2 $3ab$

3 $abc + d$

4 $\dfrac{abc}{d^2}$ 5 $\dfrac{a^2bc}{d}$

67 Pythagoras' theorem

1 Find x

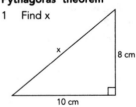

2 Find y

68 Trigonometry: Finding an angle

Find x

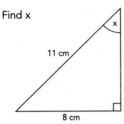

69 Trigonometry: Finding a side

1 Find x

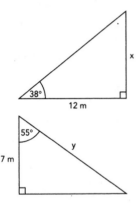

2 Find y

70 Trigonometry: Solving problems

A ship sails 300 km on a bearing of 078°.

1 How far north has the ship sailed?

2 How far east has the ship sailed?

71 Locus

1 Two points, A and B are 5 cm apart. Draw the locus of the point which is always an equal distance from A and B.

A·   · B

2   This is a plan of a building. The
    building has a force-field which
    reaches 2 m from the building.
    The scale is 1 cm represent 2 m.
    Use a dotted line to show the
    edge of the force field. Part of
    the force field is drawn for you

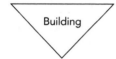

    - - - - - - - - -
    Force field

    Building

72 Designing questionnaires

1   State one advantage and one
    disadvantage of asking this
    question:

Which is your favourite subject?

2   State one advantage and one
    disadvantage of asking this
    question:

Place a tick by your favourite subject from this list	
Maths	
English	
French	
History	
Science	

73 Hypotheses

1   Kim tests the hypothesis "Boys
    watch more television than girls".
    She could present the data in a bar
    chart. Write down four other ways in
    which she could present the data.

2   How would you test these
    hypotheses? Choose from
    experiment, observation or
    questionnaire:

    a Boys' favourite colour is blue.

    b A certain die is biased.

    c Red is the most common
       colour for cars.

74 Using and drawing conclusions from graphs

This is a conversion graph to change
gallons into litres:

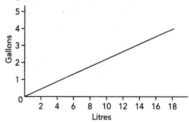

1   Convert 9 litres into gallons.

2   Convert 3 gallons into litres.

3   Convert 40 gallons into litres.

75 Frequency tables and frequency diagrams

This data shows the height of 20
adults. Height is in centimetres.

163	178	179	168	180
179	187	165	183	178
174	193	193	184	193
184	168	187	189	193

Complete the frequency table and
frequency diagram overleaf.

Height	Tally	Frequency
160-under 170	IIII	4
170-under 180		

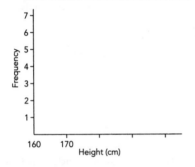

76 Comparing data

Draw a frequency polygon to illustrate the following data. Compare the distributions and comment on your findings. This table shows the rainfall in two towns. (Rainfall is in millimetres.)

Month	Hilton	Deepdale
April	20	12
May	18	15
June	16	25
July	15	32
August	15	26
September	16	18

77, 78 Mean, median, mode and range

Find the mean, median, mode and range of:

1 5, 8, 12, 5, 6

2 3, 10, 4, 10, 3, 5, 14, 12, 10, 6

79 Comparing two sets of data

This table shows the weight (in kg) of two flocks of sheep:

Flock A			Flock B		
30	45	70	52	58	64
68	52	38	80	73	74
57	78	82	76	56	62
38			74		

Use the range and mean or median to compare the two flocks.

80 Grouped data

This table shows the marks obtained by 200 students in an examination:

Mark	0-20	21-40	41-60	61-80	81-100
Frequency	0	68	36	54	42

1 What is the modal class?

2 Estimate the median.

3 Estimate the mean.

81 Cumulative frequency

This table shows the heights of 80 boys aged 15 at Upton School:

Height (cm)	Frequency
150 to 160	5
160 to 170	8
170 to 180	26
180 to 190	37
190 to 200	4

1 What is the range of the heights?

2 Draw a cumulative frequency diagram.

3 What is the median height?

4 What is the upper quartile?

5 What is the lower quartile?

6 What is the interquartile range?

82 Using cumulative frequency diagrams to compare distributions

This table shows the heights of 100 boys aged 15 at Downland School:

Height (cm)	Frequency
150 to 160	17
160 to 170	21
170 to 180	23
180 to 190	18
190 to 200	21

Draw a cumulative frequency diagram to show this information. Use the median and interquartile range to compare the boys at Downland School with the boys at Upton School in the previous question.

83, 84 Scatter diagrams

This scatter diagram shows the height and mass of eight girls aged 15:

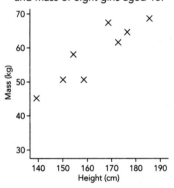

1 Describe the relationship shown by this graph.

2 Draw a line of best fit.

3 Use your line of best fit to estimate the mass of another 15 year old girl who is 170 cm tall.

85 Understanding pie charts

This pie chart shows the favourite pets of Year 11 pupils.

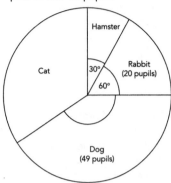

1 How many pupils are in Year 11?

2 How many pupils chose "hamster"?

3 What is the angle for "dog"?

4 How many pupils chose "cat"?

5 What is the angle for "cat"?

86 Drawing pie charts

Show this information in a pie chart:

Favourite sport	Number of pupils
Swimming	7
Fishing	12
Tennis	12
Football	9

87 The probability scale

Show the probability of the following events on the probability scale:

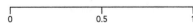

1 Shaking a six on a die. Mark with an A.

2 Shaking an even number. Mark with a B.

3 Shaking a number greater than 7. Mark with a C.

109

88 Justifying probabilities

How would you work out the probability of each of the following? Choose equally likely outcomes or experimental evidence.

1 How a coin will land.

2 How a drawing-pin will land.

3 Whether Alan or Barry is the faster runner.

89 Estimation of probability by experiment

Sarah and Jane tried an experiment. They each dropped drawing-pins from a height of 2 m. This table shows how they landed:

	Point up	Point down
Sarah	6	4
Jane	40	60

1 Which results are likely to be most reliable and why?

2 Using Jane's results estimate the number of "point up" you would expect if the experiment was carried out 10 000 times.

90 Probability: Examination-type questions

The probability of a new battery failing is 0.003.

a What is the probability of a new battery working?

b 40 000 batteries were produced. Estimate how many failed.

91, 92 Probability

1 A bag contains four red discs, four blue discs and two yellow discs. A girl is blindfolded and selects a disc. What is the probability of selecting:

a A red disc?

b A yellow disc?

c A red or a yellow disc?

2 Four coins are tossed. What is the probability of at least one head?

93 Tree diagrams

John has a 0.3 chance of passing History and a 0.4 chance of passing Geography. Draw a tree diagram to show this and hence calculate:

1 His probability of passing both subjects.

2 His probability of passing exactly one subject.

3 His probability of failing both subjects.

Answers to diagnostic tests

1

1   -5, -1, 0, 2, 3   2   -5
3   -7

2

1   48 000   2   80

3

1   4230   2   0·00382

4

1   45·98   2   5·59
3   0·1686   4   70

5

1   38 702   2   39 remainder 2

6

1   921   or   921   2   £1600 (400 x 4)
    −189   −732
    ‾732   ‾189

7

1   800 ÷ 0·02 = 40 000   2   24
3   20 000

8

1   -30·84492   2   -18·071085

9

1   6 cm   2   625
3   a   343   b   3

10

1   0·000632   2 $2·73 \times 10^5$
3   $7·2 \times 10^{-3}$ 4 $2·476 \times 10^{-4}$
                            or 0·0002476

11

1   $1\frac{1}{4}$ 2 $\frac{9}{11}$
3   $3\frac{9}{20}$

12

1   0·273   2   3·8%

13

1   3/125   2   0·375
3   80%

14

1   4:3   2   6 km

15

1   a   £250   b   £400

16

1   17·5%   2   30%
3   20%

17

1   2000   2   £254·40
                         (Note: £254·4 is wrong)
3   £219   4   £6561

18

1   a   19, 22   b   3n + 1
     c   361

19

1   a   Square numbers
     b   Cube numbers
     c   Triangle numbers
2   1, 2, 3, 5, 6, 10, 15, 30
3   11, 13, 17

20

1   2 x 2 x 2 x 5 x 7 x 7 or $2^3.5.7^2$
2   HCF 18
     LCM 180
3   $-\frac{1}{8}$ or -0·125

21

1   7y or 7 x y
2   $\frac{5}{4}$

22

1   a   18
     b   6
     c   72
2   20

23

1   y = 3   2   y = -5
3   y = 4·5   4   y = 12

Answers

24
1. $7x = 63$
2. 9

25
1. 4·7

26
1. 3·16
2. 289
3. 0·625
4. 2·4

27
1. $y = (4c)^2$ or $y = 16c^2$
2. $y = 5x$
3. $y = {}^A/_B$

28
1. 19·2
2. 0·69295
3. 0·37336
4. a 113
    b 1·27
    c 4·37

29
1. a^8
2. $12a^5$
3. $4a^{10}$
4. $20a^3x - 15a^2c$
5. $6a^3c^3d^2 + 8a^4c^4$
6. $6a^2 - 22a + 20$

30–32
1. $4a(3a - c)$
2. $5a^2c(3cd + 5a)$
3. $(a - 5)(a - 2)$
4. $a = 5, 2$

33
$a = 4, y = -2$

34

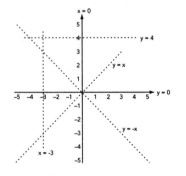

35

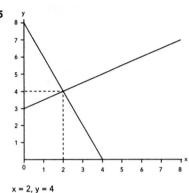

$x = 2, y = 4$

36

$y = {}^3/_2 x - 3$

37

a $y = 2x + 2$
b $y = -3x^2 + 2$
c $y = -x^3$

38
1. 13·15
2. 27 km/h (approx) (see diagram)
3. a

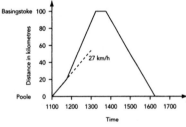

b 16:15

39
1. $x < 4$
2. $x > -2$
3. $x \geq 4$
4. $5 \leq x < 8$
5. $x \geq 2, y < 4, y > x$

40
1. 160°
2. 40°
3. 300°
4. 90°

41

1 Obtuse　　　　2 Acute
3 Reflex　　　　4 Right angle

42

1 a = 70°　　　　2 Alternate
b = 110°　　　　3 Corresponding
c = 110°
d = 70°
e = 110°
f = 70°
g = 110°

43

1 72°　　　　2 108°
3 20

44

1 286°　　　　2 106°
3 056°

45

1 Triangular prism
2

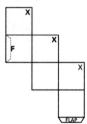

46, 47

1 Trapezium　　　　2 Rhombus
3 Isosceles triangle
4

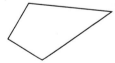

48

1 7·5 cm　　　　2 8 cm
3 2 cm

49

1

Order 4

2

Order 2

3

Order 6

4

No rotational symmetry

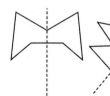

50, 51

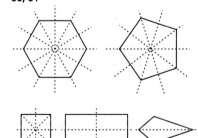

52, 53

A′ (5,4), B′ (8,4), C′ (8,1), D′ (5,1)

Answers

54

(4,2) (5,3) (6,2)

55

1 $\begin{pmatrix} 6 \\ -1 \end{pmatrix}$

2

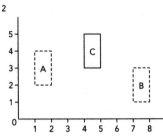

3 $\begin{pmatrix} -3 \\ -1 \end{pmatrix}$

56

1 17-20 m   2 4-5 kg

57

1 360 m   2 0·85 litres

58

Any answer between 8 m and 12 m

59

1 7·325 m

2 7·315 m

60

1 83·79 km/h   2 90 km/h

61

1 8 hours 31 minutes

2 a 5 hours 38 minutes

    b 5 hours 37 minutes 54 seconds

62

1 20°   2 a 94·2 cm

3 4·72 m   b 707 cm^2

4 352 cm^3

5 a 250 m^2

    b 75·1 m

6 Area of large circle = 201·0619298 m^2

Use all figures in calculator. Do not approximate.

Area of small circle = 78·5398163 m^2

Area of path = 122·5 m^2

63

1 20 cm^2 2 78 cm^2

3 3 cm

64

1 60 cm^3

2 2880 cm^3 or 0·00288 m^3

65

1 111 cm^2

2 62 cm

66

1 Length   2 Area

3 None of these   4 Length

5 Volume

67

1 12·8 cm   2 9·22 cm

68

46·7°

69

1 9·38 m   2 12·2 m

70

1 62·4 km   2 293 km

71

1

A ·   · B

2

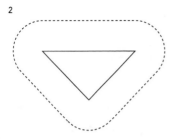

72

1 It is an open-ended question. Pupils can state their favourite subject (advantage). There may be a large number of different responses. These may be difficult to analyse and record (disadvantage).

2 It is a closed question. The subject chosen is only the favourite from the list, so it may not be the pupil's favourite (disadvantage). There are only five possible responses. This will make it easy to analyse and record the results (advantage).

73

1 Table, pie chart, frequency polygon, pictogram

2 a Questionnaire
   b Experiment
   c Observation

74

1 2 gallons   2 13·5 litres

3 180 litres

75

Height	Tally	Frequency
160-under 170	IIII	4
170-under 180	IIII	5
180-under 190	IIII II	7
190-under 200	IIII	4

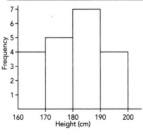

76

Hilton has a similar amount of rainfall each month, the rainfall varies in Deepdale with more rain in the middle months of June, July and August. Deepdale has more rainfall than Hilton.

77, 78

1 Mean = 7·2, median = 6, mode = 5, range = 7

2 mean = 7·7, median = 8, mode = 10, range = 11

79

Flock A	Flock B
range 52	range 28
mean 55·8	mean 66·9
median 54·5	median 68·5

The range of flock B is lower than flock A. This shows flock B is more consistent with less variation in the weight of sheep in the flock.

The mean of flock B is higher than flock A. This suggests flock B is heavier.

The median of flock B is higher than flock A. This suggests flock B is heavier.

80

1 21-40   2 58 (approx)

3 57 (approx)

81

1 50

2

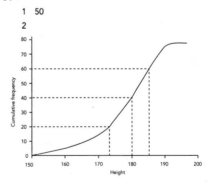

3 181 (approx)   4 186 (approx)

5 173 (approx)   6 13 (approx)

Answers

82

<u>Downland</u>

Median = 175 (approx), upper quartile = 188 (approx), lower quartile = 164 (approx), interquartile range = 24 (approx)

The median shows the middle boy at Upton School is 6 cm taller.

The interquartile range at Downland School is 24, at Upland 13. This shows the boys at Upland School vary less in height than the boys at Downland School (ie they are more closely grouped at Upland School).

83, 84

1   Positive corellation, or the taller the heavier

2   Line from about (140, 45) to (190, 70)

3   60 kg (approx)

85

1	120	2	10
3	147°	4	41
5	123°		

86

360 ÷ 40 = 9° per pupil

swimming = 63°, fishing = 108°, tennis = 108°, football = 81°

87

```
┌─────────────────────────────────────────┐
0       0·166          0·5                 1
↑        ↑              ↑
C        A              B
```

88

1   Equally likely outcomes

2   Experiment

3   Experiment

89

1   Jane's results, because she carried out the experiment more times

2   4000

90

1   a   0·997

    b   120

91, 92

1   a $^4/_{10} = ^2/_5$

    b $^2/_{10} = ^1/_5$

    c $^6/_{10} = ^3/_5$

2   $^{15}/_{16}$

93

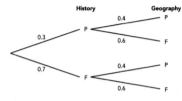

1   0·12   2   0·46

3   0·42

Index

Aa

Accuracy of measurement 59
Acute angle...41
Algebra 21-33
Angles 40-42, 67-70, 85-86
Approximation 6, 7
Area 62-66
Area of cross-section 64
At least (probability).......................................92
Aural tests (useful Maths)............................2-7
Averages..77-80
Axes of symmetry 50, 51

Bb

Bearings 44
Best fit..84
Bisect a line...71
Bisect an angle 71
Brackets.............................8, 22, 26, 28-31

Cc

Calculator keys % 16
( ) 8, 22, 28
x² 9
xʸ 9, 17
x¹ʸ 9
√ 9, 28, 62, 67
³√ 9
aᵇ𝒸 11, 13, 91
+/− 1, 9, 10, 28
EXP EE 10
D'M'S'' °'" DMS " " 61
SIN COS TAN 68, 69
M MR 8, 9
Capacity..56-58
cc..57
Centilitre 57
Centimetre 56, 57
Centre of enlargement 52-54

Cc (continued)

Centre of rotation 49
Chance (probability).......................................87
Checking..6, 7
Chord 41
Circle..41, 62
Circumference...62
Comparing data....................................76, 79, 81
Comparing distributions 82
Compasses...71
Compound measures.......................................60
Congruence 48
Constructions...71
Continuous data 59
Conversion graphs...74
Correlation 83
Corresponding angles 42
Cosine (cos) 68-70
Cross-section 64
Cube 45
Cube root..9
Cubic centimetre 57
Cubic graph 37
Cuboid..45, 63, 65
Cumulative frequency...............................81, 82
Cylinder..62

Dd

Data...72-76, 79-81, 83
Decimal...3, 4, 10, 12, 13
Density 60
Depression 70
Diagonal...46
Diameter 62
Discrete data..59
Distance, speed, time....................................38, 60, 61
Division 2-8
Drawing graphs..37
Drawing lines 34

Ee

Elevation	70
Enlargement	52-54
Equally likely outcomes	88
Equation of a straight line	36
Equations	23-27
Equations (simultaneous)	33, 35
Equations (quadratic)	25, 29-32
Equilateral triangle	47, 49, 50
Error	25, 59
Estimation	6, 7, 58
Expansion of brackets	29, 30
Experimental evidence	88, 89
Exterior angle	43

Ff

Factorisation	30-32
Factors	19, 20
Fibonacci sequence	19
Foot (feet)	56
Formula	27, 28, 62-66
Fractions	11, 13, 17
Frequency diagram	75
Frequency polygon	76
Frequency table	75

Gg

Gallon	56
Gradient	36
Gram	56, 57
Graphs	34-39, 74-76
Grouped data	80

Hh

HCF (highest common factor)	20
Hexagon	43, 49, 50
Hypotenuse	67-70
Hypothesis	73

Ii

Imperial units	56
Inches	56
Indices	9, 10, 29-32
Inequalities	39
Interior angle	43
Interquartile range	81, 82
Intersecting lines	42
Isosceles triangle	47, 51, 67

Kk

Kilogram	56, 57
Kilometre	56, 57
Kite	46, 47, 51

Ll

LCM (lowest common multiple)	20
Length	56-59, 63-66
Letters to represent numbers	21-33, 36
Line of best fit	84
Line of symmetry	50, 51
Linear graphs	37
Litre	56, 57
Locus (loci)	71
Long division	5
Long multiplication	5
Lower quartile	81, 82

Mm

Make x the subject	27
Maps	14
Mass	56-60
Maximum and minimum values	59
Mean	77-80
Measurement (accuracy)	59
Measures (compound)	60
Median	77, 79-82
Memory (calculator)	8, 9
Mental arithmetic	2-7

Metre 56, 57
Metric units 56-60
Mile 56
Millilitre 57
Millimetre 57
Modal class 80
Mode 77, 79, 80
Multiples 19, 20
Multiplication 2-7

Nn
Negative numbers 1
Nets 45
Nth term 18
Number patterns 18-20

Oo
Obtuse angle 41
Octagon.......................................43, 49, 50
Ounce 56

Pp
Parallel lines..42, 46, 48
Parallelogram......................................46, 47, 63
Patterns..18-20
Pentagon 43, 49, 50
Percentages.................12, 13, 16, 17
Perimeter 63-66
Perpendicular bisector.....................41, 71
Pie chart..85, 86
Pint...56
Polygon..43, 76
Pound...56
Powers 9, 10, 29-32
Prime factor..20
Prime number 19, 20
Prism 45, 64
Probability..87-93
Product of primes 20
Proportion..14, 15

Protractor..40, 44, 86
Pyramid 45
Pythagoras' theorem.............................41, 67

Qq
Quadratic equation 25, 29-32
Quadratic graphs.....................................37
Quadrilaterals...46
Quartiles 81, 82
Questionnaires......................................72, 73

Rr
Radius 62, 66
Range...78-82
Ratio..14, 15
Reciprocal 20
Reciprocal graphs 37
Rectangles 46, 47, 49, 51
Reflex angle 41
Regions 39
Regular polygons.....................................43
Regular shapes 43, 49, 50
Rewriting formulae.................................27
Rhombus...46, 47, 51
Right angle..41
Right-angled triangles 67-70
Roots..9
Rotational symmetry.........................43, 46, 49
Rounding 6, 7
Rule...18

Ss
Scale...14
Scale factor...48, 52-54
Scatter diagrams.................................83, 84
Sequences 18, 19
Shading regions.......................................39
Significant figures 7
Similarity...48
Simultaneous equations 33, 35

Index

Sine (sin)	68-70
Sketching curves	37
Slope	36
Solids	45
Solving equations	23-27, 33
Solving equations (using graphs)	35
Solving quadratics	25, 31, 32
Speed, time, distance	38, 60, 61
Square	46, 47, 49, 50
Square-based pyramid	45
Square number	19
Square root	9, 26-28
Squared	9, 26, 27
Standard form	10
Stone	56
Straight line equation	36
Straight line graphs	34-37
Substitution	21, 24, 25
Surveys	72, 73
Symmetry	46, 47, 49-51

Tt

Tally chart	75
Tangent (tan)	68-70
Tetrahedron	45
Three-dimensional (3-D)	45
Time	61
Time, speed, distance	38, 60, 61
Tonne	57
Transformation	52-55
Translation	52, 55
Trapezium	46, 47, 63, 64
Travel graphs	38
Tree diagrams	90, 93
Trial and improvement	25
Triangle	43, 47-51, 63, 64, 67-70
Triangle numbers	19
Triangular-based pyramid	45
Triangular prism	45

Trigonometry	67-70
Two-dimensional (2-D)	45, 49-51

Uu

Units	56-58
Upper quartile	81, 82

Vv

Vectors	55
Volume	60, 62-66

Ww

Writing equations	21, 24
Writing in algebra	24

Xx

x axis	34

Yy

y axis	34
$y = mx + c$	36
Yard	56

Zz

Z shapes	42

123

$2\pi r$, πr^2, $\pi r^2 h$	62, 66
2-D	45, 49-51
3-D	45
%	94